THIS IS YOUR BOOK

The book you hold in your hands is yours. You are the author, editor, and illustrator. See the white box on the front cover where the author's name usually goes? Write your name in that space with a permanent marker because this book is all about you and your relationship with God.

As you read *Who Am I? (And What Am I Doing Here?)* and work through the pages of this journal, you will be taking a wonderful trip. You don't need a plane ticket or a life preserver—just a pen, scissors, glue, maybe some colored pencils, and a Bible.

Of course, travelers need a good map. So to help you keep track of your voyage, you can use the lesson plan grid like a calendar, crossing off lessons as you've completed them. That way, you'll always know where you left off.

As you travel, you might want to write about what you are discovering. There are lots of blank pages in your journal for doing just that. You may even want to keep a photo or newspaper clipping to remind you of your travels. There's room for that, too.

At the end of your journal, you'll find some special pages. Where most books have the author's photo and biography, you'll find a page where you can provide your own. Who are you? Where are you from? What do you think people should know about you? Paste a current photo at the top of the page.

You'll also find several "testimonials" pages near the end. This is a great place for your fellow travelers—parents, youth pastor, family, and friends—to write a note about your book and about how you have grown during your journey.

The great thing about this journal is that you can keep it, long after your lessons are completed, to remind you of the concepts you learned along the way.

It's sure to be an exciting journey, so grab a writing utensil and let's get started!

Who Am I?
Notebooking Journal

Published by
Apologia Educational Ministries, Inc.
P.O. Box 896844
Charlotte, NC, 28289-6844
www.apologia.com

ISBN: 978-1-935495-53-6

Text: David Webb, Peggy Webb
Book Design: Andrea Martin, Doug Powell

Printed by Bradford & Bigelow, Newburyport, MA
January 2022

10 9 8 7 6 5 4

HOW TO USE THIS BOOK

Here are some general instructions for the different types of pages you'll find in your journal.

Blank Note-Taking Pages

Throughout the book you will find multiple blank pages. Use these to take notes, draw ideas, attach photos or articles, or record Bible verses as you study each lesson.

Think About It

These are questions about the story portion of the lesson. You can write your answers in the space provided or use these questions for family discussion.

Words to Know

Here you will find the vocabulary words from each lesson. Use this page to write the definition of each word and perhaps draw something that will help you remember what the word means.

Hide It in My Heart

Use this page to write out your favorite translation of the Bible verse shown on the page. Writing the verse will help you memorize it. Most of the time you will find a second memory verse page that corresponds to the *What Should I Do?* section of the lesson.

Make a Note of It

There's a page in your journal for each *Make a Note of It* box in the textbook. Use this page to record your answers as you consider how the lesson applies to your life.

Word Puzzles

Crosswords and word search puzzles help you remember important words from the lessons. In the word search puzzles, you'll be searching up, down, and diagonally only; there are no backwards words. You'll find an answer key for the puzzles on pages 201–204.

Mini Books

Your journal contains several mini books for you to assemble. These books will help you record important ideas in a visual way. You will find the mini books at the back of the journal with specific instructions on how to put them together. Attach your assembled mini book to the corresponding page in each lesson.

My Prayer

A page is provided in each lesson for you to write or draw your own prayer to God based on your hopes, your needs, and what you are learning about God, yourself, and your relationship with Him. Go back and read these pages often and watch for His answers to your prayers.

Praise Report

Use these pages to record how God is answering your prayers and how you see Him working in your life and in the lives of others. Make good use of these pages to strengthen your faith and encourage you in your journey.

I Spy!

Where have you seen God while studying this lesson? Did a particularly beautiful sunset remind you of the beauty He has created? Did your dog do something so funny that God's joy bubbled out of your heart? This is a great place to write or draw about where you have seen God.

Living Out Loud

Every few lessons, you'll find one of these pages in your journal. Use this page to record the things you have been doing to minister to others. These might be organized activities like a mission trip or working with the babies in the church nursery, or it may be something like surprising your sister by doing her chores for her one day.

Do You Remember?

Each lesson in *Who Am I?* contains a lot of information. These review pages will help you check your memory concerning important points of each lesson. Write your answers in the space provided or use the questions for family discussion time.

Find Out More

These are lists of activities, Bible stories, books, hymns, contemporary Christian songs, websites, and even movies that can help you dig deeper into the people, places, and themes you've learned about in each lesson. Be sure to add any resources you find on your own.

Lesson Plans

You can use these daily lesson plans as a guide or simply to keep track of your work. Suggestions for each day's reading and journal assignments are provided. However, the schedule is flexible and designed to allow you to work at your own pace.

Who Am I? Read pages 15–16 and discuss. Read pages 17–25, discuss. **Journal:** Take notes. Do "Think About It," page 12. Do "Why Did God Make Me This Way?" on page 13. Do "God Turned Them Back," page 14. 1	***Who Am I?*** Read page 26, discuss. Study "Words You Need to Know" and "Hide It in Your Heart." **Journal:** Take notes. Do "Words to Know," page 15. Do "Hide It in My Heart," page 16. Do "Who I Am" word search, page 17. 2	***Who Am I?*** Read pages 27–35, discuss. **Journal:** Take notes. Do "My Super Power," page 18. Assemble "Made in God's Image" mini book, pages 19 and 205–208. 3
Who Am I? Read pages 35–36, discuss. **Journal:** Take notes. Do "Created for Harmony with God," page 20. Do "Hide it in My Heart," page 21. Do "My Prayer," "Praise Report," and "I Spy," pages 22–24. 4	***Who Am I?*** Read pages 37–43, discuss. **Journal:** Take notes. Do "Do You Remember?" on pages 26–27. 5	***Who Am I?*** Read pages 44–45, discuss. **Journal:** Take notes. Do "Meet Amira" page 25. Do "God's Masterpiece" crossword pages 28–29. Do "What's the Difference?" on pages 30–31. 6
Who Am I? Read pages 46–48, discuss. Read pages 48–57, discuss. **Journal:** Take notes. Do "Think About It," pages 36–37. 7	***Who Am I?*** Read page 57. Study "Words You Need to Know" and "Hide It in Your Heart." Read "An Ugly Duckling Becomes a Swan," page 58. **Journal:** Do "Words to Know" and "Hide It in My Heart," pages 38–39. 8	***Who Am I?*** Read pages 58–62, discuss. **Journal:** Take notes. Do "I See God's Glory," page 40. Do "Whose Glory?" word search, page 41. 9
Who Am I? Read pages 62–65, discuss. Read pages 66–68, discuss. **Journal:** Take notes. Do "Choosing a Path," page 42. Do "My Psalm," page 43. Assemble "Called by God" mini book, pages 44 and 209–214. 10	***Who Am I?*** Read page 68, discuss. **Journal:** Take notes. Do "Hide it in My Heart," page 45. Do "My Prayer," "Praise Report," and "I Spy," pages 46–48. Do "Do You Remember?" on pages 50–51. 11	***Who Am I?*** Read pages 69–75, discuss. **Journal:** Take notes. Do "Meet Remy," page 49. Do "Uniquely Gifted to Give God Glory" crossword pages 52–53. Do "What's the Difference?" on pages 54–55. 12

Who Am I?
Read pages 76–78, discuss. Read pages 79–88, discuss.

Journal: Take notes. Do "Think About It," pages 60–61.

13

Who Am I?
Read pages 88–89, discuss. Study "Words You Need to Know" and "Hide It in Your Heart."

Journal: Do "Words to Know" and "Hide It in My Heart," pages 62–63.

14

Who Am I?
Read pages 90–94, discuss.

Journal: Take notes. Do "Think on These Things" word search, page 64. Do "I Wish I Hadn't Heard That," page 65. Do "Living Out Loud," page 66.

15

Who Am I?
Read pages 95–100, discuss.

Journal: Take notes. Assemble "Six In, One Out" mini book, pages 67 and 215–218. Do "Hide it in My Heart," page 68.

16

Who Am I?
Read page 101, discuss.

Journal: Take notes. Do "Every Day in the Word," page 69. Do "My Prayer," "Praise Report," and "I Spy," pages 70–72. Do "Do You Remember?" on pages 74–75.

17

Who Am I?
Read pages 102–108, discuss.

Journal: Take notes. Do "Meet Kiet," page 73. Do "Something to Think About" crossword, pages 76–77. Do "What's the Difference?" on pages 78–79.

18

Who Am I?
Read pages 109–112, discuss. Read pages 113–121.

Journal: Take notes. Do "Think About It," pages 84–85.

19

Who Am I?
Read "A Fish Story," page 121, discuss. Study "Words You Need to Know" and "Hide It in Your Heart."

Journal: Do "Words to Know" and "Hide It in My Heart," pages 86–87.

20

Who Am I?
Read pages 122–128, discuss.

Journal: Take notes. Do "A House of Worship," page 88. Do "Once More…with Feeling" word search, page 89.

21

Who Am I?
Read pages 128–132, discuss.

Journal: Take notes. Do "Hurt Feelings Café," pages 90–91. Assemble "Feelings Wheel" mini book, pages 92 and 219–222.

22

Who Am I?
Read page 132, discuss.

Journal: Take notes. Do "Hide it in My Heart," page 93. Do "My Prayer," "Praise Report," and "I Spy," pages 94–96. Do "Do You Remember?" on pages 98–99.

23

Who Am I?
Read pages 133–139, discuss.

Journal: Take notes. Do "Meet Ellie," page 97. Do "Let Wisdom Be Your Guide" crossword, pages 100–101. Do "What's the Difference?" on pages 102–103.

24

Who Am I?
Read pages 140–142, discuss. Read pages 143–150, discuss.

Journal: Take notes. Do "Think About It," page 108.

25

Who Am I?
Read and study "Words You Need to Know" and "Hide It in Your Heart."

Journal: Take notes. Do "Words to Know" and "Hide It in My Heart," pages 109–110.

26

Who Am I?
Read pages 151–155, discuss.

Journal: Take notes. Do "The Choices I Made," page 111. Do "Decisions, Decisions" word search, page 112. Do "What's in This Stuff?" on page 113.

27

Who Am I?
Read pages 156–161, discuss.

Journal: Take notes. Assemble "Choose Wisely" mini book, pages 114 and 223–226.

28

Who Am I?
Read page 161, discuss.

Journal: Take notes. Do "Hide It in My Heart" page 115. Do "My Prayer," "Praise Report" and "I Spy," pages 116–118. Do "Do You Remember?" on pages 120–121.

29

Who Am I?
Read pages 162–169, discuss.

Journal: Take notes. Do "Meet Dev," page 119. Do "I'm a Child of the King!" crossword, pages 122–123. Do "What's the Difference?" on pages 124–125.

30

Who Am I?
Read pages 170–172, discuss. Read pages 173–181, discuss.

Journal: Take notes. Do "Think About It," pages 130–131. Do "Nature's Footprints," pages 132–133.

31

Who Am I?
Study "Words You Need to Know" and "Hide It in Your Heart."

Journal: Take notes. Do "Words to Know" and "Hide It in My Heart," pages 134–135.

32

Who Am I?
Read pages 181–186, discuss.

Journal: Take notes. Do "Christ Is My Covering," page 136. Do "Eyes on the Prize" word search, page 137. Do "Living Out Loud," page 138.

33

Who Am I?
Read pages 187–192, discuss.

Journal: Take notes. Do "If We Truly Believed," page 139. Assemble "Go for the Win!" mini book, pages 140 and 227–230.

34

Who Am I?
Read pages 192–193, discuss.

Journal: Take notes. Do "Hide it in My Heart," page 141. Do "My Prayer," "Praise Report," and "I Spy," pages 142–144. Do "Do You Remember?" on pages 146–147.

35

Who Am I?
Read pages 194–200, discuss.

Journal: Take notes. Do "Meet Sage," page 145. Do "Run to Win!" crossword, pages 148–149. Do "What's the Difference?" on pages 150–151.

36

Who Am I?
Read pages 201–203, discuss. Read pages 204–212.

Journal: Take notes. Do "Think About It," pages 156–157.

37

Who Am I?
Study "Words You Need to Know" and "Hide It in Your Heart."

Journal: Take notes. Do "Words to Know" and "Hide It in My Heart," pages 158–159.

38

Who Am I?
Read pages 212–218, discuss.

Journal: Take notes. Do "The Good Samaritan," page 160. Do "Against Such Things There Is No Law" word search, page 161.

39

Who Am I?
Read pages 219–224, discuss.

Journal: Take notes. Do "The Boaz Principle," page 162. Do "Nurturing Your Fruit," page 163. Assemble the "Fruit of the Spirit" mini book, pages 164 and 231–236.

40

Who Am I?
Read page 224, discuss.

Journal: Take notes. Do "Hide it in My Heart," page 165. Do "My Prayer," "Praise Report," and "I Spy," pages 166–168. Do "Do You Remember?" on pages 170–171.

41

Who Am I?
Read pages 225–231, discuss.

Journal: Take notes. Do "Meet Jin-Ho," page 169. Do "How Does Your Garden Grow?" crossword, pages 172–173. Do "What's the Difference?" on pages 174–175.

42

Who Am I?
Read pages 232–234, discuss. Read pages 235–245, discuss.

Journal: Take notes. Do "Think About It," pages 180–181.

43

Who Am I?
Study "Words You Need to Know" and "Hide It in Your Heart."

Journal: Take notes. Do "Words to Know" and "Hide It in My Heart," pages 182–183.

44

Who Am I?
Read pages 245–249, discuss.

Journal: Take notes. Do "What the Bible Says About Saint…," pages 184–185. Do "Who I Am in Christ" word search, page 186.

45

Who Am I?
Read pages 249 through the end of "You Are a Winner," page 254, discuss.

Journal: Take notes. Do "What Can God Do For Me?" on page 187. Assemble "You Are Someone New!" mini book, pages 188 and 237.

46

Who Am I?
Read page 254, discuss.

Journal: Take notes. Do "Hide It in My Heart," page 189. Do "My Prayer," "Praise Report," and "I Spy," pages 190–192. Do "Do You Remember?" on pages 194–195.

47

Who Am I?
Read pages 255–262, discuss.

Journal: Take notes. Do "Meet Mei," page 193. Do "Victory in Christ" crossword, pages 196–197. Do "What's the Difference?" on pages 198–199.

48

WHAT ARE WE DOING HERE?

THINK ABOUT IT
SASHA'S CHOICE

1. Where does this story take place? Do you think the story takes place in a modern place and time? Why? Why not?

2. Sasha was born with a crippled foot that makes it difficult for him to walk or run. How does this affect the way Sasha sees himself? How does it affect the way other people see him?

3. Why is Sasha's mother worried about sending him to school for the first time?

4. What kinds of problems does Sasha face by the time he's ready for school?

5. Why does Sasha not want to go to the front of the classroom to introduce himself? How does he show bravery in this situation?

6. After the family discussion about bearing God's image, do you think Sasha will ever again struggle with his handicap? Why? Why not?

7. Have you ever been teased for something? How did it make you feel? How did you respond? Have you ever teased someone? If so, how do you think you made that person feel?

Make a Note of it

WHY DID GOD MAKE ME THIS WAY?

In the story "Sasha's Choice," Sasha learned that he was created by God to be unique and that neither his birth nor his lame foot was an accident. What is it about the way you were made that you've sometimes wished you could change? Have you ever considered thanking God for making you this way?

God Turned Them Back

Write a poem or short story or draw a story in pictures about how God might use a natural force to thwart an enemy that suddenly invaded your home town. Could it be torrential rain? Hip-deep snow? A plague of mosquitoes?

Words to Know

PARABLE

IMAGE

IMAGE-BEARER

CHRISTLIKE

Hide it in My Heart

Write your favorite translation of the verse below and memorize it.

For we are God's masterpiece. He has created us anew in Christ Jesus, so we can do the good things he planned for us long ago.

Ephesians 2:10, NLT

THERE'S NO GOD LIKE MINE!

U E O M N I P O T E N T E T O F C K L T
Q I K L K F J Z V M A M E Z P S H O U J
T F M O M N I S C I E N T I O E R C S X
P L N A P G V Z W Z P M G K M C I X P T
E B Q S G S U I A W M B O F N R S U K X
R Y M Y K E H H N T I R D H I E T N Q I
S L H V V V H U C G V V S W P T L C W M
O X O N D F I T Y I X V M O R I I C Z A
N F L J A Q Z Z U H F A A K E D K J Z G
C Y Y T V R U S S I A L S E S E E E G E
W O R L D V I E W E A U T E E N P C D B
S K Y H K N W V L E S A E T N T S T M E
U U Z S V U F B L H A B R E T I O R Q A
P O R M V H A B P H N L P R O T C M M R
E T B S L T A A S M P E I N K Y G T Y E
R T Z H U R S A C R I I E A G K A T A R
M I J M A N S O E Y U A C L R R H T T P
A Z M P T F Q R W N O X E C R W I R B A
N I H A E N O R M A N R O C K W E L L Q
L Q A T I S N M I R R O R Y R H X E W P

Russia
parable
image
image-bearer
Christlike
Superman
secret identity
God's masterpiece
Norman Rockwell
eternal
immutable
omnipresent
omnipotent
omniscient
holy
person
worldview
valuable
mirror
Sasha

My Super Power

Like Clark Kent, do you have a special gift or talent that few people know about? What can you do better than anyone you know? Have you thanked God for this gift? Write down several ideas for how you can use this gift to reflect God's glory and show His love to others.

Mini Book
Made in God's Image

Find the instructions on page 205.
Attach your finished mini book here.

Make a Note of it
CREATED FOR HARMONY WITH GOD

Instead of becoming more like Jesus, people often look for other ways to feel better about themselves and find lasting peace. Will money bring you personal harmony? Will the right clothes? Will shinier hair, a prettier face, or bigger muscles give you peace? Will the number of friends you have? Why can't these things bring you the lasting personal harmony God created you to enjoy?

HIDE IT IN MY HEART

Write your favorite translation of the verse below and memorize it.

AND THE LORD—WHO IS THE SPIRIT—MAKES US MORE AND MORE LIKE HIM AS WE ARE CHANGED INTO HIS GLORIOUS IMAGE.

2 CORINTHIANS 3:18, NLT

My Prayer

Praise Report

I Spy

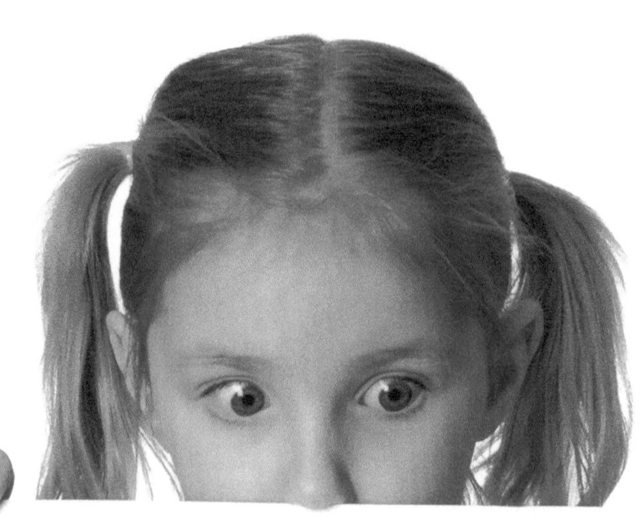
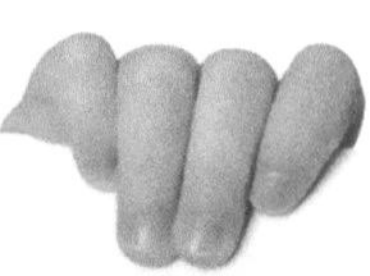
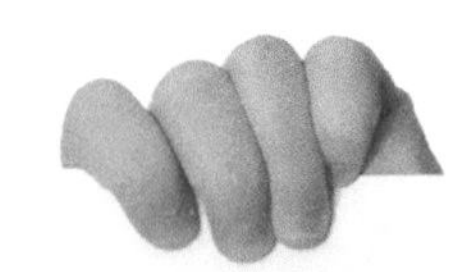

Meet Amira

Based on what you've learned about Amira and her beliefs, draw a picture of her doing an everyday task. Or write a poem, story, or song about her or a conversation you might have with her.

Do You Remember?

1. What makes you special as an individual? How do you know?

2. When did God first know your name and when you would be born? When did you begin to be a part of His plans?

3. Why weren't you born in ancient times or the distant future?

4. Whom else should people see when they look at you?

5. Are your eyes the same color as God's? Why or why not?

6. What does it mean to be made in the image of God?

7. How are you like God?

8. How are you *not* like God?

9. As a child of God, whom are you supposed to become more like every day?

10. What makes every human life sacred?

GOD'S MASTERPIECE

Word List

Napoleon
Sasha
parable
image
image-bearer
Christlike
Clark Kent
breath
Norman Rockwell
eternal
immutable
Jesus Christ
omnipresent
omnipotent
omniscient
holy
everything
personal being
biblical
burkha
Mecca
mosque
Allah

Across

5. Adjective that means "in agreement with God's Word"
6. A visual representation of something or someone
7. Never changing
11. "The Spirit of God has made me; the ______ of the Almighty gives me life." (Job 33:4)
13. A person who carries, or bears, the likeness of God
14. Existing everywhere at once, yet separate from creation
15. He illustrated more than 300 covers for *The Saturday Evening Post*
17. His army was turned back from their invasion of Russia by cold weather in 1812
18. A short story that contains biblical truths for our lives
19. Knowing all things
20. Never sinning
22. All powerful
23. Traditional robe for a Muslim woman

Down

1. Being like Jesus in character, spirit, or deed
2. Muslims believe he is the one true God
3. It's the familiar form of the Russian name Aleksandr
4. "_____ ______ is the same yesterday and today and forever"(Hebrews 13:8)
8. Superman's secret identity
9. When Muslims pray, they bow in the direction of this Saudi Arabian city
10. Someone who has a mind, emotions, a will, a conscience, creativity, and a spirit
12. Having no beginning and no end
16. "For God is greater than our hearts, and he knows __________" (1 John 3:20)
21. Islamic house of worship

WHAT'S THE DIFFERENCE?
ISLAM

1. How is the way Amira lives different from the way you live? How are your lives similar?

2. Why do you think Amira is so careful to make *dua*, eat the right foods, and participate in the ritual prayers throughout the day?

3. Find a photo of a woman wearing a *burkha*. A burkha is an outer garment worn by some Muslim women for the purpose of hiding the face and body and maintaining their modesty when out in public. Women wear it over their daily clothing and remove it when they return to the sanctuary of their household, out of the view of men who are not their husbands or close relatives. Not long ago, the president of a major European country proposed a law that would ban the wearing of burkhas in public. He said this type of clothing cuts women off from all social life and takes away their identity. What do you think of the burkha?

4. What do you think visiting a mosque would be like? What would Amira think of your church if she visited it?

5. How is Amira's view of Allah different from the biblical Christian view of God?

6. The word *Islam* means "to submit," and a *Muslim* is "one who submits" to Allah. How is this similar to the beliefs of Christians?

7. Amira's father kneels on a special prayer rug because he wants the area where he is praying to be clean. Do you do anything special when you pray? Do you prefer to sit or kneel or stand? Do you hold your hands in a specific way? Why?

8. Many Muslim girls are not allowed to study the Qur'an. Why not? How do you think God sees men differently from women? How are they the same in His eyes?

9. What are the five pillars of Islam?

10. Which of the five pillars resemble Christian beliefs? How are they similar to the beliefs you practice? How are they different?

11. The Qur'an teaches that Allah is completely unlike the people he created. How is this different from the biblical Christian view of God?

12. How is the way Amira sees herself different from the way you see yourself as a child of God?

Find Out More

Things to do

- Ask your parents why they chose your name. Look up your name online or in a baby-name book and discover the meaning of your name.

- Find out the Russian equivalent of your name. Is there a "familiar" or "diminutive" form of this name? How would someone in Russia address you formally using your father's name?

Books

How Big Is God? by Lisa Bergren (ages 3–8)
The Crippled Lamb by Max Lucado (ages 3–8)
The Tale of Three Trees: A Traditional Folktale by Angela Elwell Hunt (all ages)
Eyewitness: Russia by Kathleen Berton Murrell (ages 9–13)
Norman Rockwell's America by Christopher Finch (all ages)
Girl Politics: Friends, Cliques, and Really Mean Chicks by Nancy Rue (ages 9–12)
What Do We Know About Islam? by Sharukh Husain (ages 9–12)
Islam and the Bible by David Goldmann (teens and adults)

Songs

"Who Am I?" by Mark Hall
"Wait and See" by Brandon Heath
"Things We Leave Behind" by Michael Card
"How Great Thou Art" by Stuart Hine
"I Am" by Eddie James
"El Shaddai" by Michael Card and John Thompson

WHAT WILL YOU MAKE TODAY?

Think About It
The Pocket Knife

1. What kind of church does Sasha's family attend? How does Sasha's church seem different from your church? How are they similar?

2. In his sermon, Father Yakov teaches that every person has been given a special talent or ability. What does he say we are supposed to do with our gifts?

3. How does Sasha discover his gift?

4. How does Brother Pavel show wisdom in the way he responds to Sasha's taking his pocket knife to church?

5. In what way is Mr. Kerensky, the master woodcarver, more than just a teacher to Sasha?

6. How does Sasha begin to change as a result of the time he spends learning to carve wood?

7. If you were to give a Christmas gift to Jesus, what might it look like?

8. How do you think this experience will affect the way Sasha thinks of himself, especially his height and his crippled foot? Will he ever worry about such things again? Why or why not?

Words to Know

CREATIVITY

CHRISTIANITY

CALLING

HUMILITY

Hide It in My Heart

Write your favorite translation of the verse below and memorize it.

WHATEVER YOU DO, WORK AT IT WITH ALL YOUR HEART, AS WORKING FOR THE LORD, NOT FOR MEN, SINCE YOU KNOW THAT YOU WILL RECEIVE AN INHERITANCE FROM THE LORD AS A REWARD.

COLOSSIANS 3:23–24

Make a Note of It
I See God's Glory

God is the Great Artist, and His technique is visible in the essence of everything we see. Indeed, His very image is in every person we meet. Take a moment to look around you today and enjoy the beauty of His creation. Then draw or paint a picture or take a photograph of someone or something that reveals His glory to you.

WHOSE GLORY?

H T B P G C N B Q L G P T A L E N T S R

O J M O U R A N Q C R E A T I V I T Y C

E T G C A R T Q M I R A C L E S U R D S

B O L K R A I B A N N A P A V L O V A T

Y Y O E K B V I N C E N T V A N G O G H

O T R T O I I T Q A V Z Q V G Z C O K X

T H Y K F L T T O W E R O F B A B E L D

A E T N T I Y P N D R C C J B F O I C H

B G O I H T U C X S T P A M A L T X P U

E R G F E I G R J K H I L L E I R T H M

R E O E C E I E V W X E H G L E H T O I

N A D I O S C C L C L T N I V I L G L L

A T W D V H A H J A J A H R R T N X Y I

C A S T E X L E Z B L C A Q M P D G S T

L R D V N C T E S E A C R T E T E I P Y

E T P N A U B I H B D R Z S U Y A R I D

F I L A N M A C H O H J I H H C N D R K

X S E X T O I H O H A P P I N E S S I F

E T O X L M W W G Z H E C Y K V E G T R

C H R I S T I A N D L U X B Q J E Z A T

The Great Artist
pocket knife
woodcarver
crèche
nativity
Anna Pavlova
creativity

Bezalel
Ark of the Covenant
tabernacle
Christian
calling
Holy Spirit
talents

abilities
Michelangelo
Pietà
Tower of Babel
Bach
Vincent van Gogh
glory to God

happiness
humility
miracles

Make a Note of it
CHOOSING A PATH

Write a poem, a song, or a short story about two friends, both of whom are extremely talented. They might be singers or dancers or musicians or another kind of performer. One uses his or her gift for the glory of God; the other uses his or her gift to pursue fame and fortune. Write about which of the two has chosen the best path. Which of them ends up happier? Why?

Make a Note of It
My Psalm

Sometimes we write and sing songs or paint pictures or take photographs to help us remember important truths that we tend to forget over time. King David did this often and called them psalms. Write a psalm that reflects three or more of the attributes of God you learned about in Lesson 1.

Mini Book
Called by God

Find the instructions on page 209.
Attach your finished mini book here.

HIDE IT IN MY HEART

Write your favorite translation of the verse below and memorize it.

EACH OF YOU HAS RECEIVED A GIFT TO USE TO SERVE OTHERS.

1 PETER 4:10, NCV

My Prayer

Praise Report

I Spy

MEET REMY

Based on what you've learned about Remy and his beliefs, draw a picture of him doing an everyday task. Or write a poem, story, or song about him or a conversation you might have with him.

Do You Remember?

1. What three important qualifications made Bezalel worthy to build the Ark of the Covenant and God's tabernacle?

2. What does it mean to have a "calling" on your life?

3. What's the best way to discover your God-given abilities?

4. Where do your talents and abilities come from? What then must you use these talents to do?

5. What does the Latin phrase *Soli Deo Gloria* mean?

6. Some people can use their talents to create beautiful works of art, but not every gift from God can be so easily seen. What kind of abilities can a person have that are harder to see?

7. Is it wrong to feel good when you do something well, win an award, or accomplish a goal? Why not?

8. According to 1 John 2:16, why can't owning many nice things or achieving goals make you permanently happy? What makes you valuable as a person?

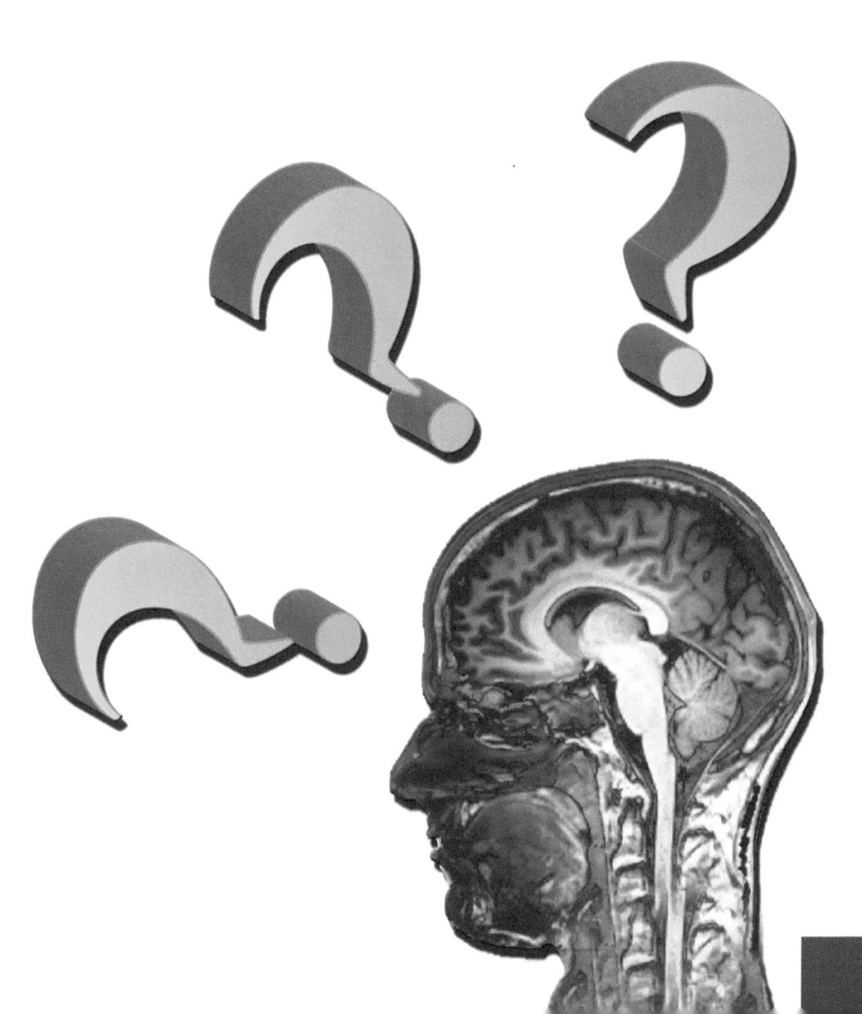

UNIQUELY GIFTED TO GIVE GOD GLORY

Word List

King David
created
crèche
Christian
calling
Anna Pavlova
Bezalel
priesthood
rewards
The Pietà
Tower of Babel
Johann Sebastian Bach
stress ball
Big Bird
creativity
happiness
outward
humility
Montreal
recycling
cello
St. Matthew Passion
"Invictus"

Across

3. Being creative is about honoring God and giving this to others
4. He sang, "Don't worry that it's not good enough for anyone else to hear"
5. "Man looks at the _______ appearance, but the Lord looks at the heart" (1 Samuel 16:7)
6. Another word for a nativity scene
9. He spent the last 27 years of his life composing church music in Leipzig
11. A follower of Jesus
14. Bach's oratorio that tells the story of Christ's crucifixion from the Gospel of Matthew
16. The first person in the Bible said to have been filled with the Holy Spirit
17. Remy's instrument of choice
18. "In the beginning, God _______" (Genesis 1:1)
20. God's purpose for your life, for which He has gifted you and chosen you
21. He danced with all his might before the Lord in 2 Samuel
22. The people of Shinar built it for their own glory, not for God's

Down

1. God "______ those who earnestly seek him" (Hebrews 11:6)
2. "But you are a chosen people, a royal __________, a holy nation, a people belonging to God" (1 Peter 2:9)
6. The ability to express your thoughts and imagination for the glory of God
7. Poem that declares every man is the master of his fate and the captain of his soul
8. Squeezable toy used to help relieve tension or exercise the muscles of the hand
10. World's most famous ballerina during the early 20th century
12. An attitude in your heart that you are not better than any other person
13. Remy's home town
15. The processing of used materials into new products
19. The only piece of art that Michelangelo ever signed

WHAT'S THE DIFFERENCE?
HUMANISM

1. How is the way Remy lives different from the way you live? How are your lives similar?

2. Remy works hard to develop his musical talent. What does he hope to do with this talent? Why does he want to be a successful musician?

3. How is the way Remy sees his talent different from the way you see your gifts as a child of God?

4. Remy's friend Andre tells him that good people go to heaven. Can a person be "good enough" to get into heaven? What does the Bible say we need to do to have everlasting life?

5. What does Remy's father teach him about what makes a person successful? How is this different from what the Bible teaches about success?

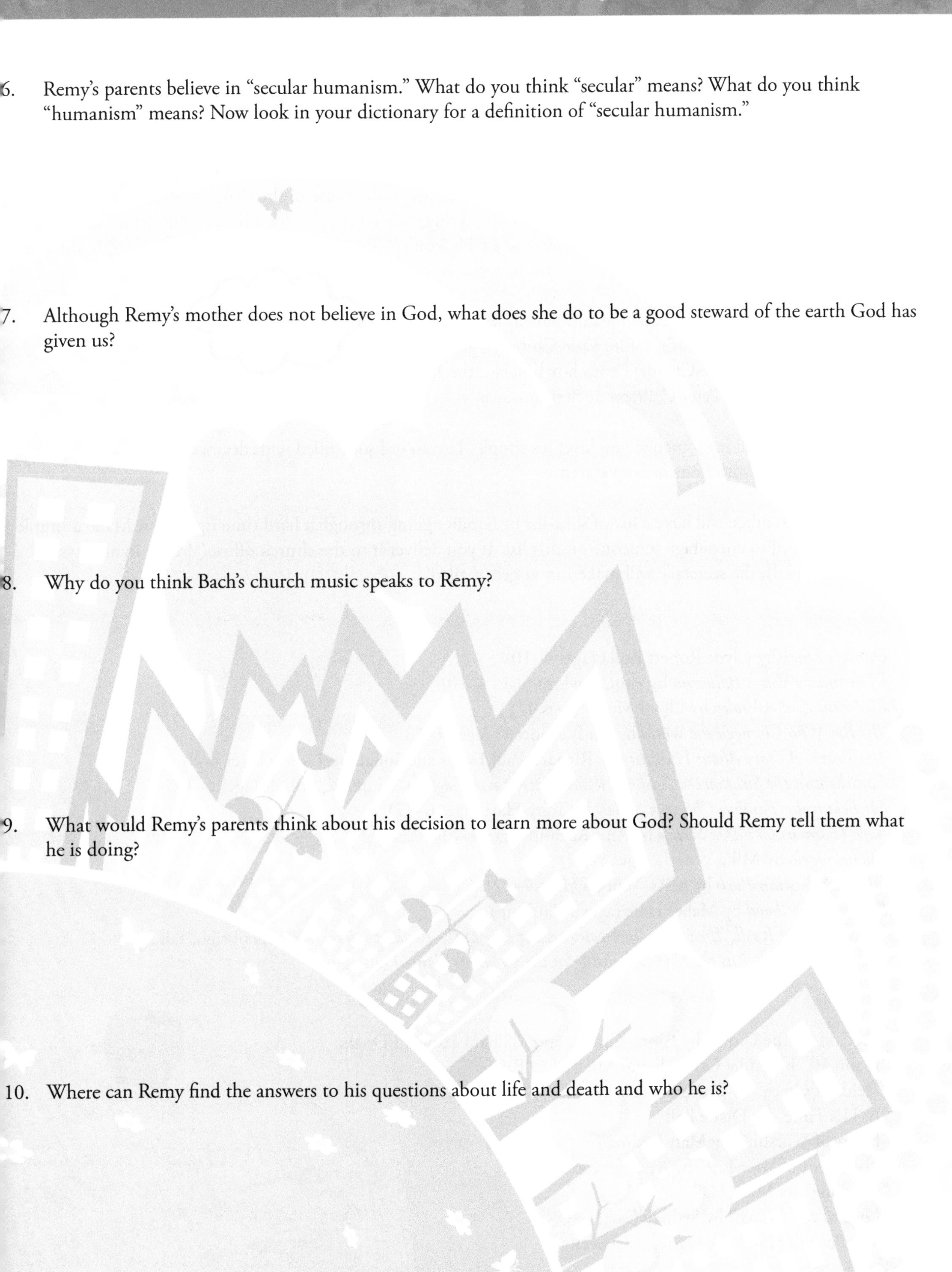

6. Remy's parents believe in "secular humanism." What do you think "secular" means? What do you think "humanism" means? Now look in your dictionary for a definition of "secular humanism."

7. Although Remy's mother does not believe in God, what does she do to be a good steward of the earth God has given us?

8. Why do you think Bach's church music speaks to Remy?

9. What would Remy's parents think about his decision to learn more about God? Should Remy tell them what he is doing?

10. Where can Remy find the answers to his questions about life and death and who he is?

Find Out More

Things to Do

- Carving and whittling are fun skills, but they can be dangerous because of the sharp implements used to cut the wood. For a fun and safe experience, try soap carving. Ask your mom for a bar of plain white soap and lightly draw a shape on its plain side. Then use a table knife to slowly carve away everything outside the lines. You'll find that even a simple shape requires patience and diligence!

- Research some of the more unique and offbeat uses of creativity in our culture such as the Longaberger Basket Building in Newark, Ohio; Dale Chihuly's glass installations; the large-scale environmental works of Christo and Jeanne-Claude; bento box lunches; the Randy's Donut Shop's donut in Los Angeles; or the paper sculptures of Peter Callesen or Bert Simons.

- Make a stress ball for someone you love! It's simple. Use an old sock filled with dry rice. Or you can try using a balloon filled with flour or corn starch.

- Your church office will have a list of shut-ins or families going through a hard time right now. Make a simple greeting card to encourage someone on this list. If you deliver it to the church office (already in an envelope and stamped), the secretary will make sure it gets mailed.

Books

Daniel's Duck by Clyde Robert Bulla (ages 4–10)
I Dreamed I Was a Ballerina by Anna Pavlova (ages 4–10)
Zin! Zin! Zin! A Violin by Lloyd Moses (ages 4–8)
The Boy Who Changed the World by Andy Andrews (ages 4–10)
The Tower: A Story About Humility by Richard Paul Evans and Jonathan Linton (ages 4–8)
Camille and the Sunflowers: A Story About Vincent van Gogh by Laurence Anholt (ages 6–12)
Michelangelo (Famous Children Series) by Tony Hart (ages 6–12)
Bach (Famous Children Series) by Ann Rachlin (ages 4–8)
Michelangelo by Mike Venezia (ages 9–12)
Johann Sebastian Bach by Mike Venezia (ages 9–12)
Beautiful Girlhood by Mabel Hale (ages 12 and up)
The Wonder of It All: The Creation Account According to the Book of Job by Ric Ergenbright (all ages)
The Hand That Paints the Sky: Delighting in the Creator's Canvas (all ages)

Songs

"To God Be the Glory" by Fanny Crosby and William Howard Doane
"Psalm 40" by Eddie Carswell and Michael O'Brien
"Fields of Grace" by Darrell Evans
"In His Time" by Diane Ball
"Heart of Worship" by Matt Redman
"The Poem of Your Life" by Michael Card
"LifeSong" by Mark Hall
"Lord of the Dance" by Sydney Carter
"The Potter's Hand" by Darlene Zschech

WHAT'S ON YOUR MIND?

Think About It
The Wooden Bird

1. Why is Sasha excited about the possibility of teaching Ivan to carve?

2. How did Mr. Kerensky show wisdom when he asked Mr. Yushenko about the possibility of Ivan learning to carve?

3. How would you describe Ivan's relationship with his father?

4. What was the gift Ivan carved for his mother? What does his father say about the spoon? How does Ivan respond to his father's criticism?

5. Ivan wants to carve as well as Sasha right away instead of being patient and learning how. Have you ever wanted something right away that took you time to learn? Were you able to stick with it until you learned it?

6. Why does Ivan take Sasha's bird carving and pretend that it's his? How long does Ivan enjoy his father's compliment? Why?

7. How does Mr. Kerensky compare a crude, unfinished woodcarving to a person's sinful heart? What does he say about how a heart can be changed into something beautiful?

8. What do you think is beginning to happen in Ivan's heart and life? Why?

Words to Know

TRANSFORM

RENEW

MEDITATION

Hide It in My Heart

Write your favorite translation of the verse below and memorize it.

FINALLY, BROTHERS, WHATEVER IS TRUE, WHATEVER IS NOBLE, WHATEVER IS RIGHT, WHATEVER IS PURE, WHATEVER IS LOVELY, WHATEVER IS ADMIRABLE—IF ANYTHING IS EXCELLENT OR PRAISEWORTHY—THINK ABOUT SUCH THINGS.

PHILIPPIANS 4:8

THINK ON THESE THINGS

N	G	S	X	Q	C	M	E	H	C	W	B	R	A	I	N	L	Q	A	O
T	R	A	N	S	F	O	R	M	K	O	U	L	J	C	E	I	H	C	E
I	R	V	Y	B	E	A	U	T	I	F	U	L	W	D	Y	L	P	L	M
K	V	N	T	H	O	U	G	H	T	S	H	R	O	X	F	F	B	U	E
C	H	A	R	A	C	T	E	R	P	R	U	M	A	C	D	A	C	A	D
B	U	P	T	H	E	T	H	I	N	K	E	R	E	G	R	P	Z	L	I
P	E	A	C	E	O	N	U	G	Q	L	W	U	Y	O	E	U	A	T	T
C	C	H	O	I	C	E	S	I	O	D	D	T	N	G	J	O	M	N	A
Z	O	A	N	I	N	V	B	R	I	D	Z	O	H	D	S	M	U	B	T
A	D	M	I	R	A	B	L	E	M	D	H	I	Z	Q	K	F	Q	S	I
O	Z	S	V	K	S	A	P	R	A	I	S	E	W	O	R	T	H	Y	O
G	A	R	B	A	G	E	I	N	G	A	R	B	A	G	E	O	U	T	N
K	H	F	E	D	J	E	D	K	I	S	M	L	W	W	Y	D	O	B	U
C	G	A	C	S	L	F	Q	W	N	O	U	P	F	E	W	G	Z	Q	Z
L	K	I	N	M	T	W	S	O	A	T	E	P	L	E	A	S	A	N	T
H	K	T	V	I	L	A	I	W	T	V	X	N	O	B	L	E	Z	P	A
T	U	H	U	N	O	T	K	C	I	P	U	R	E	N	E	W	E	D	H
H	R	F	F	D	O	J	U	M	O	E	X	C	E	L	L	E	N	C	E
X	M	U	A	M	O	W	J	E	N	N	H	A	L	O	V	E	L	Y	J
P	F	L	E	G	X	J	K	B	G	S	G	R	I	G	H	T	R	S	I

brain
mind
thoughts
choices
emotions
The Thinker
transform

renewed
meditation
true
noble
right
pure
lovely

admirable
peace
imagination
"garbage in,
garbage out"
character
role model

beautiful
excellence
praiseworthy
pleasant
faithful
courageous
honorable

MAKE A NOTE OF IT
I WISH I HADN'T HEARD THAT!

Think of a time recently when you saw a movie (or read a book or heard a song) that made you feel uncomfortable. What was it that bothered you about it? Did the program (or book or song) use inappropriate language or imagery? Did the writer express some truths that made you uncomfortable? Or did the writer present ideas that you knew were not true according to God's Word? Are you more likely to seek out or avoid other works by the same artist?

Living Out Loud

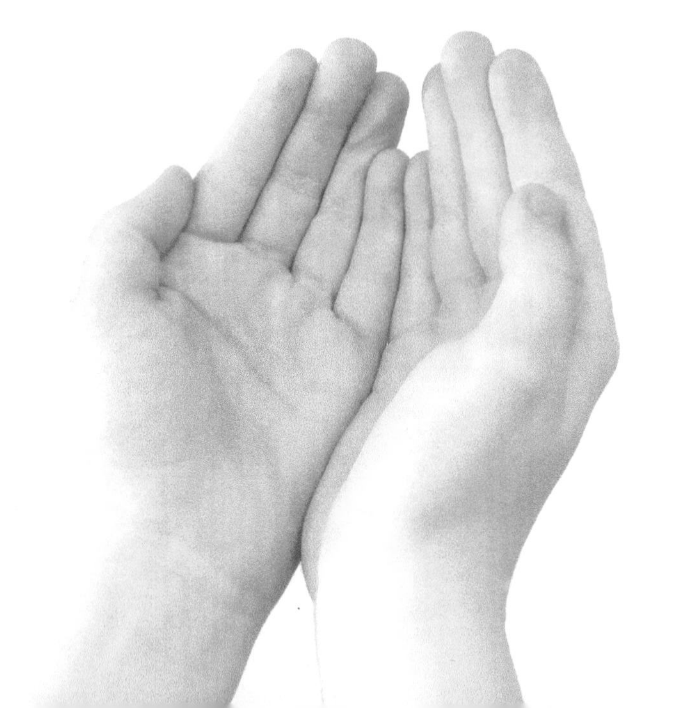

Mini Book
SIX IN, ONE OUT
Part 1

Find the instructions on page 215.
Attach your finished mini book here.

Hide It in My Heart

Write your favorite translation of the verse below and memorize it.

BE ANXIOUS FOR NOTHING, BUT IN EVERYTHING BY PRAYER AND SUPPLICATION, WITH THANKSGIVING, LET YOUR REQUESTS BE MADE KNOWN TO GOD; AND THE PEACE OF GOD, WHICH SURPASSES ALL UNDERSTANDING, WILL GUARD YOUR HEARTS AND MINDS THROUGH CHRIST JESUS.

PHILIPPIANS 4:6-7, NKJV

Every Day in the Word

Keeping a chart is a great way to remember to meditate on the Bible! Create a calendar by inserting the dates below for the current month. Then each day, write the Bible verses on which you meditate in that day's square. Can you spend time meditating on God's Word every day for a whole month?

Sunday	Monday	Tuesday	Wednesday	Thursday	Friday	Saturday

My Prayer

PRAISE REPORT

I Spy

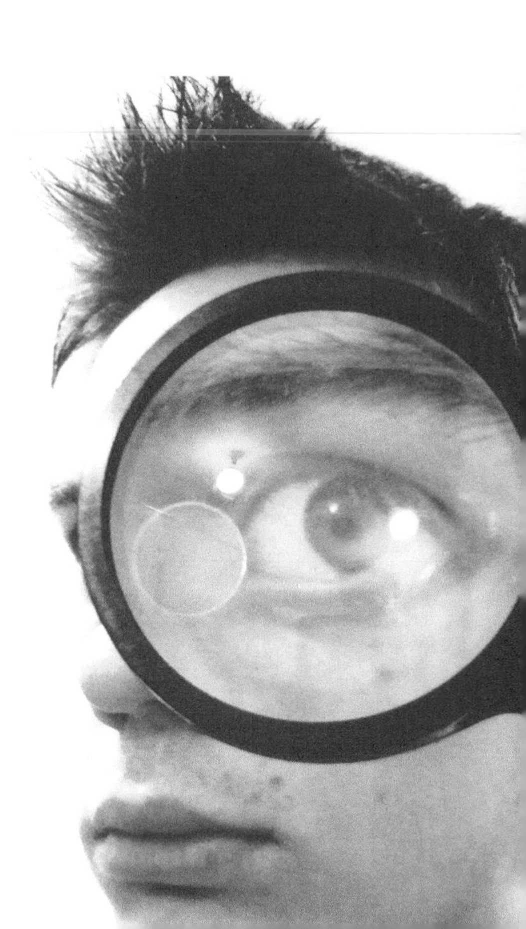

Meet Kiet

Based on what you've learned about Kiet and his beliefs, draw a picture of him doing an everyday task. Or write a poem, story, or song about him or a conversation you might have with him.

Do You Remember?

1. What is the difference between "wanting" something and "needing" something?

2. How can the things you think about affect other people?

3. How does the phrase "garbage in, garbage out" apply to your mind?

4. According to Matthew 12:34–35, how do good and evil things become stored inside us?

5. How have Christians been transformed into new people? Why is it important to understand that, as a believer, you are a new creation in Christ?

6. What are some of the things that hiding God's Word in your heart will do for you?

7. Where is the one place you can be sure to find things that are true, noble, right, pure, lovely, and admirable?

8. Why should you not dwell on negative thoughts? How can spending time with positive people lift you up?

9. Why is it a good idea to write about what you meditate on and what God speaks to your heart?

SOMETHING TO THINK ABOUT

Word List

Butter Week
ruble
Gutzon Borglum
Auguste Rodin
imagination
"garbage in, garbage out"
overflow
The Screwtape Letters
Sir Thomas Malory
corrupts
role model
transform
renewing
meditation
pure
lovely
honeycomb
truth
noble
amulet
enlightened one
Four Noble Truths
Songkran
karma

Across

1. He designed Mount Rushmore National Memorial
3. "Bad company _______ good character" (1 Corinthians 15:33)
4. To change completely
6. He sculpted "The Thinker"
8. Adjective describing one who displays outstanding character, high ideals, or godly behavior
9. Clean, chaste, and holy
12. Buddha's name means this
14. C. S. Lewis book written in the form of letters from one demon to another
15. You use it every time you draw a picture or write a story
16. Buddha's philosophy of the meaning of life
18. Necklace worn by Kiet for protection and good fortune
19. A person who sets an example of behavior that is imitated by others
21. Jesus said, "For out of the ________ of the heart the mouth speaks" (Matthew 12:34)
23. Thai New Year

Down

1. A computer term meaning if you input faulty data, your results will also be faulty
2. Another name for the Russian holiday Maslenitsa
5. Russian coin
7. He wrote *Le Morte d'Arthur* about the Knights of the Round Table
10. Ideas that are factual, real, and reliable
11. "Pleasant words are like a _________, sweetness to the soul and health to the bones" (Proverbs 16:24, NKJV)
13. Thinking deeply about God and His Word
17. "Be transformed by the _________ of your mind" (Romans 12:2)
20. Adjective meaning beautiful in spirit, deed, or form
22. Buddhist belief that everything a person does, good or bad, has natural consequences

WHAT'S THE DIFFERENCE? BUDDHISM

1. How is the way Kiet lives different from the way you live? How are your lives similar?

2. What are some ways Kiet shows respect to his parents and grandparents? What is a "wai"?

3. Kiet wears an amulet that he believes protects him from harm. As Christians, what do we believe protects us from harm?

4. In the story of Buddha, why do you think Siddhartha left his comfortable home to find the meaning of life? Where can you find the meaning of life?

5. How do Buddha's Four Noble Truths compare to what the Bible teaches? What are the differences? What are the similarities?

6. How is Buddhist meditation different from the kind of meditation the Bible teaches?

7. Why do you think Kiet's family is so careful to follow Buddhist traditions? What does the Bible teach about "earning" your way to heaven?

8. How is the Buddhist concept of reincarnation different from what the Bible teaches about life and death?

9. What do you think of the Buddhist concept of karma, the idea that we are each punished or rewarded by the universe for our actions? What does the Bible say about what we deserve for our sins? What did God do to save us from what we deserve?

10. The Buddhist religion is unusual in that Buddhists do not worship a god as most other religions do. How does this differ from the biblical Christian view of God?

Find Out More

Things to do

Mount Rushmore may be the most famous mountainside carving in America, but there are several more. Find photos online or in your library of the Crazy Horse memorial in the Black Hills of South Dakota, Stone Mountain in Georgia, and Pratt Rocks in the Catskills Mountains of New York.

Books

Who Carved the Mountain?: The Story of Mount Rushmore by Jean L. S. Patrick (ages 4–8)
Adam Raccoon and the Flying Machine by Glen Keane (ages 4–8)
Think About These Things by Ric Ergenbright (all ages)
The Screwtape Letters by C. S. Lewis (teens and adults)
Biblical Meditation for Spiritual Breakthrough by Elmer Towns (teens and adults)
The Lotus and the Cross: Jesus Talks with Buddha by Ravi Zacharias (teens and adults)

Songs

"This Is My Father's World" by Maltbie D. Babcock
"What a Friend We Have in Jesus" by Joseph Scriven
"He Reigns" by Steve Taylor and Peter Furler
"Garbage In" by Tal & Acacia
"Think on These Things" by Bob Hartman and Ronny Cates
"A Pure Heart" by Rusty Nelson
"Thy Word" by Michael W. Smith and Amy Grant

CAN YOU TRUST YOUR FEELINGS?

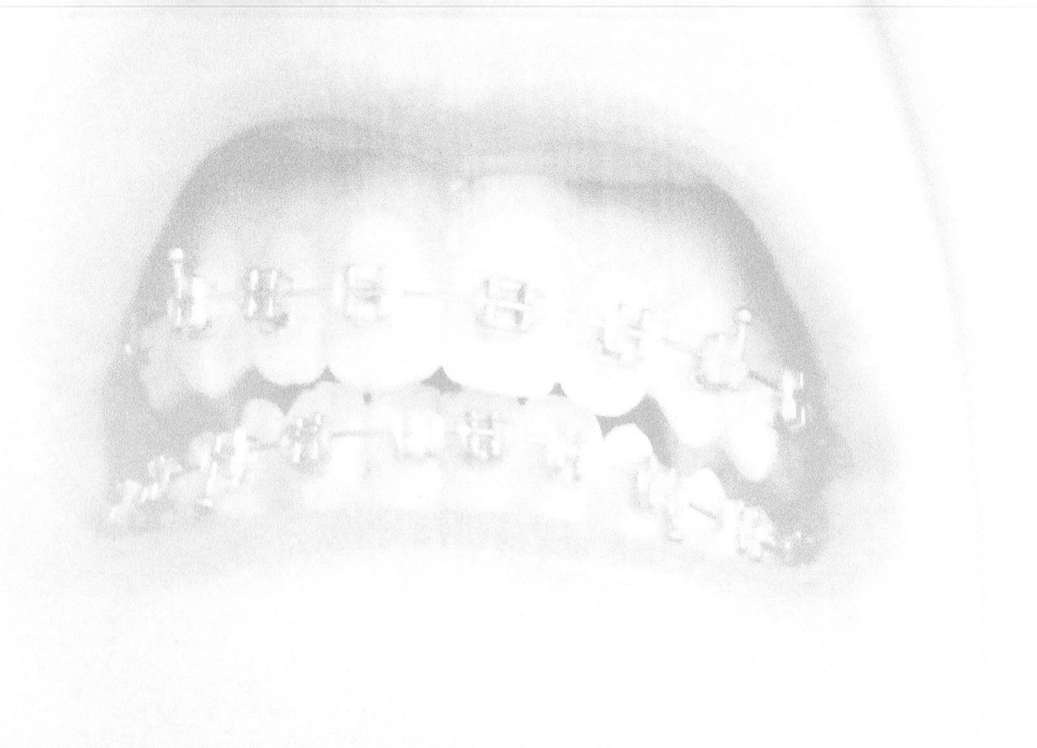

Think About It
The Altar

1. What kinds of feelings does Ivan have trouble controlling? How has this contributed to his becoming a bully?

2. Think about the relationship between Mr. Yushenko and his son, Ivan. Do you think Mr. Yushenko loves his son?

3. If Mr. Yushenko loves Ivan, why is he "relieved" when Ivan is invited to go away for the summer?

4. Why do you think Mr. Kerensky takes such a personal interest in helping Ivan? What does Ivan find out about Mr. Kerensky on the fishing trip? Were you surprised to learn that Mr. Kerensky had been in prison? Why?

5. What does Mr. Kerensky want to communicate to Ivan about the changes in his heart since he accepted Jesus as his Savior?

6. Why does Mr. Kerensky stop working on his carving of the Last Supper while the wood is still rough and unsmooth? How does he say we are all like rough blocks of wood?

7. What do you think Ivan sees in Mr. Kerensky that encourages him to believe in Jesus and trust Him as his Savior?

8. What do you think Ivan's life will be like when he returns home after being with Sasha and Mr. Kerensky all summer? Why?

Words to Know

IMPULSE

WISDOM

Hide It in My Heart

Write your favorite translation of the verse below and memorize it.

Patience is better than strength. Controlling your temper is better than capturing a city.

Proverbs 16:32, NCV

Make a Note of It
A House of Worship

Read John 2:13–17. This is the story of how Jesus cleared the moneychangers from the temple. What emotion did He express during this incident? Jesus fashioned a whip of cords and drove the men and their animals out of the temple, overturning the moneychangers' tables and dumping their money all over the floor. Why do you think He took such dramatic action instead of simply teaching against the practice of buying and selling in the temple? Do you think Jesus sinned that day? Why not?

ONCE MORE... WITH FEELING

P	P	E	A	C	E	J	J	E	A	L	O	U	S	Y	P	M	X	W	N
B	T	E	R	R	O	R	V	C	O	N	F	I	D	E	N	C	E	G	A
A	D	I	X	C	P	D	I	S	T	R	E	S	S	E	R	B	V	U	E
T	E	P	G	A	N	X	I	E	T	Y	W	A	R	M	T	H	U	V	R
I	G	E	A	O	R	H	A	P	P	I	N	E	S	S	A	Z	O	A	C
A	M	H	E	R	E	L	I	E	F	M	N	V	M	Y	O	L	R	Z	D
Y	G	R	I	E	F	D	E	B	D	O	E	F	U	B	F	R	Y	I	H
M	B	J	C	U	R	I	O	S	I	T	Y	L	V	D	Z	Z	S	P	A
S	B	V	Y	M	Q	D	I	S	C	O	U	R	A	G	E	M	E	N	T
A	O	P	E	O	Q	S	N	Y	A	S	N	P	O	N	C	U	A	U	E
D	R	L	M	S	A	N	G	E	R	O	P	P	I	S	C	F	R	N	R
N	E	E	C	C	K	J	L	G	I	U	C	X	R	F	V	H	Z	P	E
E	D	A	I	Z	L	P	A	T	I	E	N	C	E	I	E	J	O	L	O
S	O	S	S	V	Z	Q	C	E	X	F	A	Y	U	B	D	A	F	L	D
S	M	U	U	H	T	E	N	D	E	R	N	E	S	S	J	E	R	C	Y
A	N	R	A	M	F	G	D	E	L	I	G	H	T	Z	L	O	A	R	R
C	X	E	H	F	R	F	N	S	N	U	G	S	I	E	K	Y	Y	O	O
L	Q	L	A	T	C	M	T	H	G	C	O	M	P	A	S	S	I	O	N
C	X	K	K	F	D	Q	Z	J	N	E	X	C	I	T	E	M	E	N	T
J	G	U	I	L	T	S	X	S	O	R	R	O	W	S	X	F	O	T	A

patience
compassion
delight
grief
anxiety
excitement

terror
jealousy
anger
hate
joy
love

distress
sadness
peace
boredom
fear
guilt

happiness
confidence
warmth
pleasure
sorrow
pride

relief
affection
curiosity
tenderness
melancholy
discouragement

Make a Note of It
HURT FEELINGS CAFÉ

Imagine that you and a friend have had a huge fight that has left you feeling angry and frustrated. Be specific as to what you're fighting about. Then sit down and make a detailed list of possible actions you can take in response. Write your list in the style of a restaurant menu. Include both negative, destructive reactions and positive, constructive options you can choose from. Be sure to include little things you can do to help you cool down or just feel a little better. Now examine what the Bible teaches about dealing with anger and add these commands to your menu. When you are finished, look over the menu and choose a "healthy meal" of five or six items that will help you deal with your anger and resolve the problem in a positive, healthy way.

Hurt Feelings Café

menu

Positive, Constructive Choices

Biblical Choices

Negative, Destructive Choices

Mini Book
FEELINGS WHEEL

Find the instructions on page 219.
Attach your finished mini book here.

Hide It in My Heart

Write your favorite translation of the verse below and memorize it.

Be joyful always; pray continually; give thanks in all circumstances, for this is God's will for you in Christ Jesus.

1 Thessalonians 5:16–18

My Prayer

Praise Report

I Spy

Meet Ellie

Based on what you've learned about Ellie and her beliefs, draw a picture of her doing an everyday task. Or write a poem, story, or song about her or a conversation you might have with her.

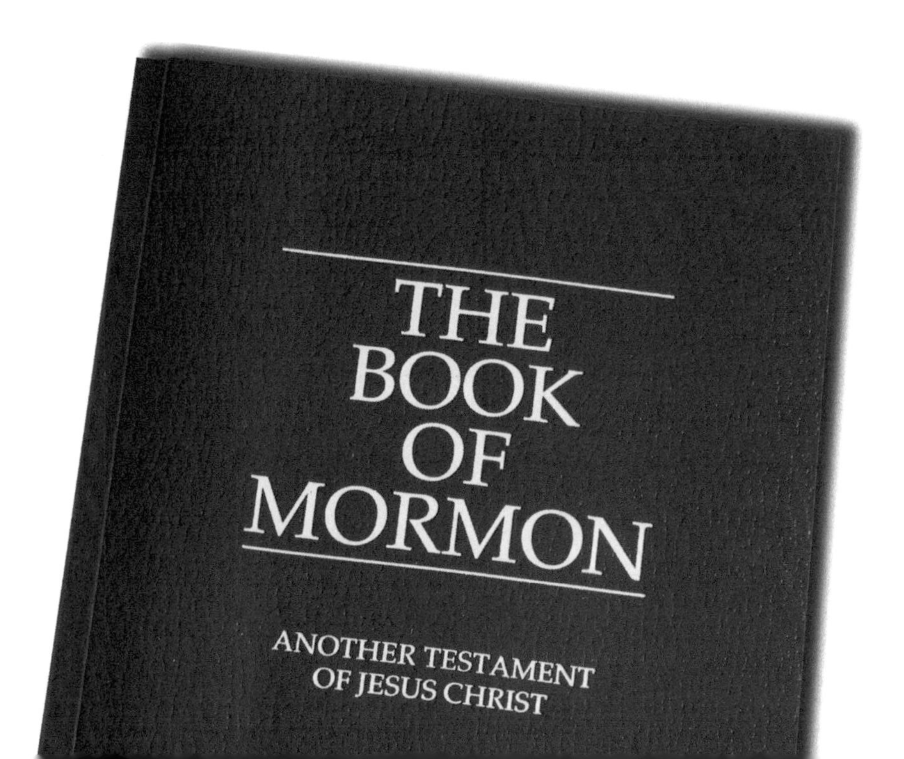

Do You Remember?

1. Why did God give us feelings?

2. Is it a sin to be angry or to feel hatred? Why not?

3. According to Jeremiah 17:9 and Proverbs 28:26, why is "follow your heart" not a good strategy for living?

4. What is an impulse? Why is it not a good idea to act on your impulses?

5. What is wisdom? Where can you go to find wisdom?

6. How do you know that Jesus understands what you're feeling? When Jesus was in emotional pain, whom did He talk with?

7. How was Jesus able to overcome His emotions?

8. What do unpleasant emotions tell us we need to do?

9. What is the best remedy for when you're feeling sad?

10. What is the difference between happiness and joy?

LET WISDOM BE YOUR GUIDE

Word List

King Kong
King Solomon
The Last Supper
impulse
fishermen
Ichthus
emotions
anxious
anger
deceitful
Gethsemane
Vulcan
praise
grief
Lazarus
temper
Judas
Salt Lake City
genealogy
temple recommend
polygamy
tithing
Mormon Church

Across

1. The Christian "fish" seen on millions of car bumpers
7. Put on "a garment of ______ instead of a spirit of despair" (Isaiah 61:3)
11. Giant ape who "fell" for an actress
13. Leonardo da Vinci's famous mural of Jesus and His disciples
14. He betrayed Jesus to the authorities
17. Deep sorrow usually brought on by the loss of a friend or loved one
19. Profession of Peter, James, and John
21. Star Trek planet where inhabitants are taught to suppress their emotions
22. "The heart is ________ above all things" (Jeremiah 17:9)
23. Also known as the Church of Jesus Christ of Latter-day Saints

Down

2. You must have this special pass to enter a Mormon temple
3. The study of a family's history
4. "Controlling your ______ is better than capturing a city (Proverbs 16:32, NCV)
5. The practice of giving ten percent of your income to your church
6. Olive grove where Jesus prayed the night of His arrest
8. A sudden or spontaneous urge to do something you hadn't planned to do
9. He wrote that there's "a time to weep and a time to laugh" (Ecclesiastes 3:4)
10. Ellie's home town
12. The practice of having more than one wife or husband
15. "Do not be _______ about anything" (Philippians 4:6)
16. The Lord is "slow to _____ and rich in love" (Psalm 145:8)
18. They're a gift from God
20. Jesus wept at the death of this brother of Mary and Martha

WHAT'S THE DIFFERENCE?
MORMONISM

1. How is the way Ellie lives different from the way you live? How are your lives similar?

2. What is the Book of Mormon? Who was Joseph Smith?

3. What do you think visiting a Mormon meetinghouse or temple might be like? What would Ellie think of your church if she visited it?

4. Why do you think Ellie's family is so careful to follow Mormon teachings?

5. What does it mean to be "excommunicated"? What does the Bible say about who decides who goes to heaven?

6. Why does the Mormon church teach that its members aren't allowed to drink alcohol or Coke, use tobacco, or watch R-rated movies?

7. Why do some Mormons believe it's a good idea to have large families?

8. The Mormon Church teaches that by living righteously, believers may one day become gods themselves, like Jesus Christ. How does this differ from the biblical Christian view of God and heaven?

9. Quoting from Genesis, Jesus said, "A man will leave his father and mother and be united to his wife, and the two will become one flesh" (Matthew 19:5). Not three or four or more, but two people, man and wife. Yet Jacob, David, and Solomon all took more than one wife, and each time it led to grief. Why do you think the early Mormons believed in polygamy? What do you think it would be like to have several mothers?

10. What is tithing? The Mormon church teaches that tithing is extremely important. What does the Bible say about tithing?

11. How are Mormon missionaries different from most Christian missionaries? Who are the missionary families your church supports?

Find Out More

Books

Today I Feel Silly: And Other Moods That Make My Day by Jamie Lee Curtis and Laura Cornell (ages 4–8)
H Is for Hook: A Fishing Alphabet by Judy Young and Gary Palmer (ages 4–8)
Fishing with Dad: Lessons of Love and Lure from Father to Son by Michael J. Rosen (ages 4–8)
Adam Raccoon in Lost Woods by Glen Keane (ages 4–8)
Leonardo da Vinci (Famous Children Series) by Ann Rachlin (ages 8–12)
Jazz Off-Key by Dandi Daley Mackall (ages 9–12)
My Feelings Are Like Wild Animals! How Do I Tame Them? by Gary Egeberg (teens)
Leonardo: The Last Supper by Pinin Brambilla Barcilon and Pietro C. Mariani (teens and adults)
The Facts on the Mormon Church by John Ankerberg, John Weldon, and Dillon Burroughs (teens and adults)

Songs

"It Is Well with My Soul" by Horatio G. Spafford
"Tell It to Jesus" by Jeremiah E. Rankin
"Empty Me" by Chris Sligh, Clint Lagerberg, and Tony Wood
"Get Down" by Tyler Burkum, Ben Cissell, Bob Herdman, Will McGinniss, and Mark Alan Stuart
"Gone Fishin'" by Adam Agee, Cody Pellerin, Jordan Messer, and Taylor Sitera

WILL YOU CHOOSE WISELY?

Gartner Tal
Wolfratshauser H.
Grahntal
Schrofen
s'Bergle
Handschuh
Unt. Schafkopf
2819

Think About It
The Feast

1. Brandon's story takes place in the year 1354, during what we call the Middle Ages, or medieval times. How did daily life during the Middle Ages differ from the way we live today?

2. What is Brandon's job at the castle? Why must he answer to Quentin? Why does Quentin call him a "varlet"?

3. Why does Gwyneth say she is a daughter of the King?

4. Most squires were not allowed to become knights until their twenty-first birthday, yet William is only nineteen when he becomes a knight. How did he earn this honor? What gave William the courage to take up the Baron's sword in battle?

5. What important character trait does Quentin lack according to William? Why does William choose Brandon to be his squire?

6. Brandon dreams of becoming a great knight in the king's service, yet when William asks him to be his squire—the next step toward becoming a knight—Brandon feels undeserving of the honor. Why does he feel this way?

7. Baron John de Lisle was a real person. He fought in the Hundred Years' War and was one of the founding members of the Order of the Garter. Cambridge Castle was also a real place. Find the city of Cambridge on a map of England. Do you know what Cambridge is most famous for today?

Words to Know

God's will

Fear of the Lord

Hide It in My Heart

Write your favorite translation of the verse below and memorize it.

Even before he made the world, God loved us and chose us in Christ to be holy and without fault in his eyes.

Ephesians 1:4, NLT

MAKE A NOTE OF IT
THE CHOICES I MADE

List five decisions you've made today. Now write a brief paragraph about each of these decisions: What were your options? Why did you choose the way you did? What were the consequences of your decision? For example: Let's say you decided what to eat for breakfast this morning. What were your possible choices? Did you make your choice based on flavors, nutritional content, the color of the box it came in, your energy needs for the day, or a combination of factors? How did your decision work out for you? Did you have good energy all morning? Or did you get hungry again an hour before lunchtime?

DECISIONS, DECISIONS

```
P R Y R R S W I S E C H O I C E S Q K F
D R X K D E O T S D Y C U W D V G Q R E
E O A V G T S L R L V K V A M X L L A A
C Y I Y Y Q G P O U D J Q R T P S O J R
I A V G E N R A O M T P N N N Q P G A O
S L L K C R E J R N O H Y I E G O O D F
I T C J O B M K U D S N H N W E T D I T
O Y H F U R A W N B B I I G Z E C S L H
N R I T N E R U D C A Q B S N K R W E E
S E L Q S A Y T E O D W Y I B E O I M L
K V D K E D A M R N V R B G L I L L M O
A E O N L O N P S S I A H N D I A L A R
G R F O O F D G T E C A Q S R Q T X M D
J E G W R L M F A Q E L O E S D X Y M N
R N O L S I A N N U I O Z J C H O S E N
H C D E R F R U D E F A I T H F U L Z E
G E N D D E T I I N A Q A W G T C M D S
B Y N G L Z H U N C L W I S D O M I P D
J D I E V L A O G E T L G F M I U G X T
T I R G Y X S A H S A T I J B G W A V M
```

Bread of Life
God's will
fear of the Lord
chosen
royalty

child of God
decisions
faithful
responsibility
wise choices
warning signs

consequences
truth
knowledge
understanding
dilemma
Cabinet
counselors

advice
guide
prayer
Solomon
wisdom
Mary and Martha
reverence

Make a Note of It

What's in This Stuff?

Go to your cupboard or kitchen pantry and find a box of breakfast cereal. If you don't eat cereal, any packaged food product will do. Write down the complete list of ingredients listed on the side of the box. Now, with the help of a parent, go to the Internet or your library and look up each one of the ingredients. Find out what it is and what it does. Are there any health warnings or advisories connected with this ingredient? If so, talk with your parents about replacing the cereal with a healthier alternative.

Mini Book
CHOOSE WISELY

Find the instructions on page 223.
Attach your finished mini book here.

Hide It in My Heart

Write your favorite translation of the verse below and memorize it.

The fear of the Lord is the beginning of wisdom, and knowledge of the Holy One is understanding.

Proverbs 9:10

MY PRAYER

PRAISE REPORT

I Spy

MEET DEV

Based on what you've learned about Dev and his beliefs, draw a picture of him doing an everyday task. Or write a poem, story, or song about him or a conversation you might have with him.

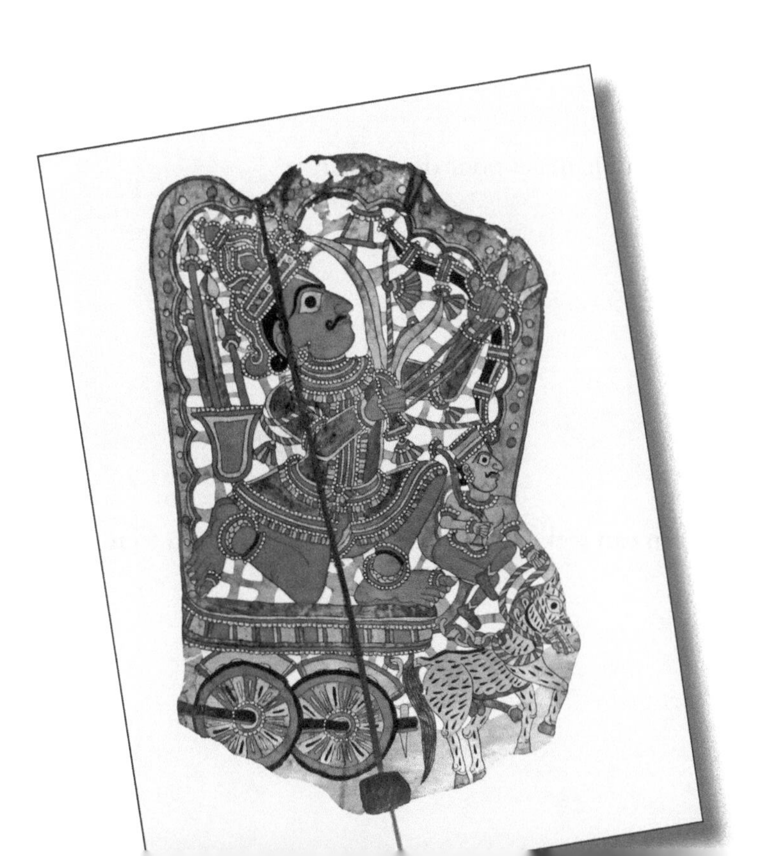

Do You Remember?

1. Who makes you royalty? How did this happen?

2. What can you do to make God love you more?

3. What are some of decisions other people make that affect you each day? Why aren't you qualified to make these decisions for yourself?

4. What are some reasons people make poor decisions?

5. What are some ways you can seek God when you have a decision to make?

6. Why is it important to seek wise counsel? Where can you find trustworthy counselors in your life?

7. How can you put Jesus first in everything you say and do?

8. What is "the fear of the Lord"?

I'M A CHILD OF THE KING!

Word List

Cheshire Cat
knights
Order of the Garter
hauberk
Fear of the Lord
Uncle Sam
beginnings
understanding
King Saul
Holy Spirit
King Solomon
John F. Kennedy
The Cabinet
Abraham Lincoln
generously
Bethany
Mary
revere
New York City
mantra
Brahman
reincarnation
Bhagavad Gita
curry

Across

1. Dev's home town
4. The youngest man ever elected to be U.S. president
6. "To God belong wisdom and power; counsel and ____________ are his" (Job 12:13)
7. Spicy Indian dish of rice, lentils, and vegetables
11. Alice asked him for directions
15. Hindus believe that all paths to faith eventually lead to it
17. The Bible says He will guide you into all truth (John 16:13)
18. "The people should not think that small ___________ are unimportant" (Zechariah 4:10, NCV)
20. "It is the Lord your God you must follow, and him you must ______" (Deuteronomy 13:4)
22. He was president during the Civil War
23. An attitude of reverence toward God

Down

2. Baron John de Lisle was one of its founding members
3. One of Hinduism's holiest books
5. A knee-length tunic made of chainmail
8. Group of 15 men and women chosen to advise the U.S. president
9. The Hindu cycle of rebirth
10. She chose the best, and Jesus said it would not be taken from her
12. They were known as "gentleman soldiers"
13. He was punished by God for consulting a psychic
14. Fictional character famously painted by James Montgomery Flagg
16. He had the good sense to ask for wisdom
18. Mary and Martha lived there
19. "If any of you lacks wisdom, he should ask God, who gives ___________" (James 1:5)
21. A Hindu chant recited to honor the gods

WHAT'S THE DIFFERENCE? HINDUISM

1. How is the way Dev lives different from the way you live? How are your lives similar?

2. Dev's family prays often. How often do you pray? What does the Bible say about how often we should pray?

3. What do you think visiting a Hindu temple might be like? What would you expect to see there? What would Dev think of your church if he visited it?

4. Dev and his family meditate and chant to empty their minds of thought as part of their Hindu beliefs. What other religion have you learned about that teaches this type of meditation?

5. The Hindu religion has many gods. A belief in more than one god is called *polytheism*. What does the Bible say about how many gods there are?

6. Hindu gods and goddesses are depicted in many unusual ways in statues and paintings. Ganesha has the head of an elephant, Hanuman is a monkey, Vishnu has four arms, and Brahma (not to be confused with Brahman) has four heads—and that's after losing one! What does the Bible say about the practice of making statues of gods? According to the biblical Christian worldview, what does God the Father look like?

7. Dev's yoga teacher says that some people just enjoy the physical benefits of yoga. What does he say is the true purpose of yoga? What does the Bible teach about how we can "get in touch" with God?

8. Who or what is Brahman according to the Hindu faith? Hindus believe that in order to become one with Brahman, they must first understand that people are not really individuals with bodies, thoughts, and feelings. How does this compare with what the Bible teaches about each person?

9. Dev is taught that people are trapped in a constant cycle of rebirth called reincarnation. What does this mean for the way Dev lives each day?

10. How does Dev's teacher describe "nirvana"? How is this like or unlike what the Bible teaches about heaven?

11. If Dev's sister lived in India, her parents may have decided to choose a husband for her, as is the Hindu tradition. What would that be like, having such an important decision made for you? How is the Christian wedding ceremony different from a Hindu wedding?

12. Dev wears a special thread as a reminder of his commitment to study Hinduism and to keep his thoughts and actions pure and righteous. What do you do to remind yourself of your commitment to live a godly life?

Find Out More

Books

The Making of a Knight: How Sir James Earned His Armor by Patrick O'Brien (ages 4–8)
His Little Princess by Shari Rose Shepherd (ages 4–10)
His Mighty Warrior by Shari Rose Shepherd (ages 7–12)
A Girl After God's Own Heart by Elizabeth George (ages 8–12)
His Princess by Shari Rose Shepherd (teens and adults)
Castle by David Macaulay (ages 9 and up)
Abraham Lincoln by Ingri and Edgar Parin d'Aulaire (ages 4–10)
Abe Lincoln Grows Up by Carl Sandburg (ages 12 and up)
Wisdom on . . . Making Good Decisions by Mark Matlock (teens)
Don't Jump to Conclusions Without a Bungee Cord by Martha Bolton (teens)
Thirteen Days/Ninety Miles: The Cuban Missile Crisis by Norman Finkelstein (young adults)

Songs

"Give of Your Best to the Master" by Howard B. Grose
"A Child of the King" by Harriet Buell
"A Mighty Fortress Is Our God" by Martin Luther
"Voice of Truth" by Steven Curtis Chapman and Mark Hall
"Majesty" by Jack Hayford
"Great Adventure" by Steven Curtis Chapman
"We Don't Need It" by Rebecca St. James,
Bill Deaton & Blair Masters

HOW WILL YOU RUN THE RACE?

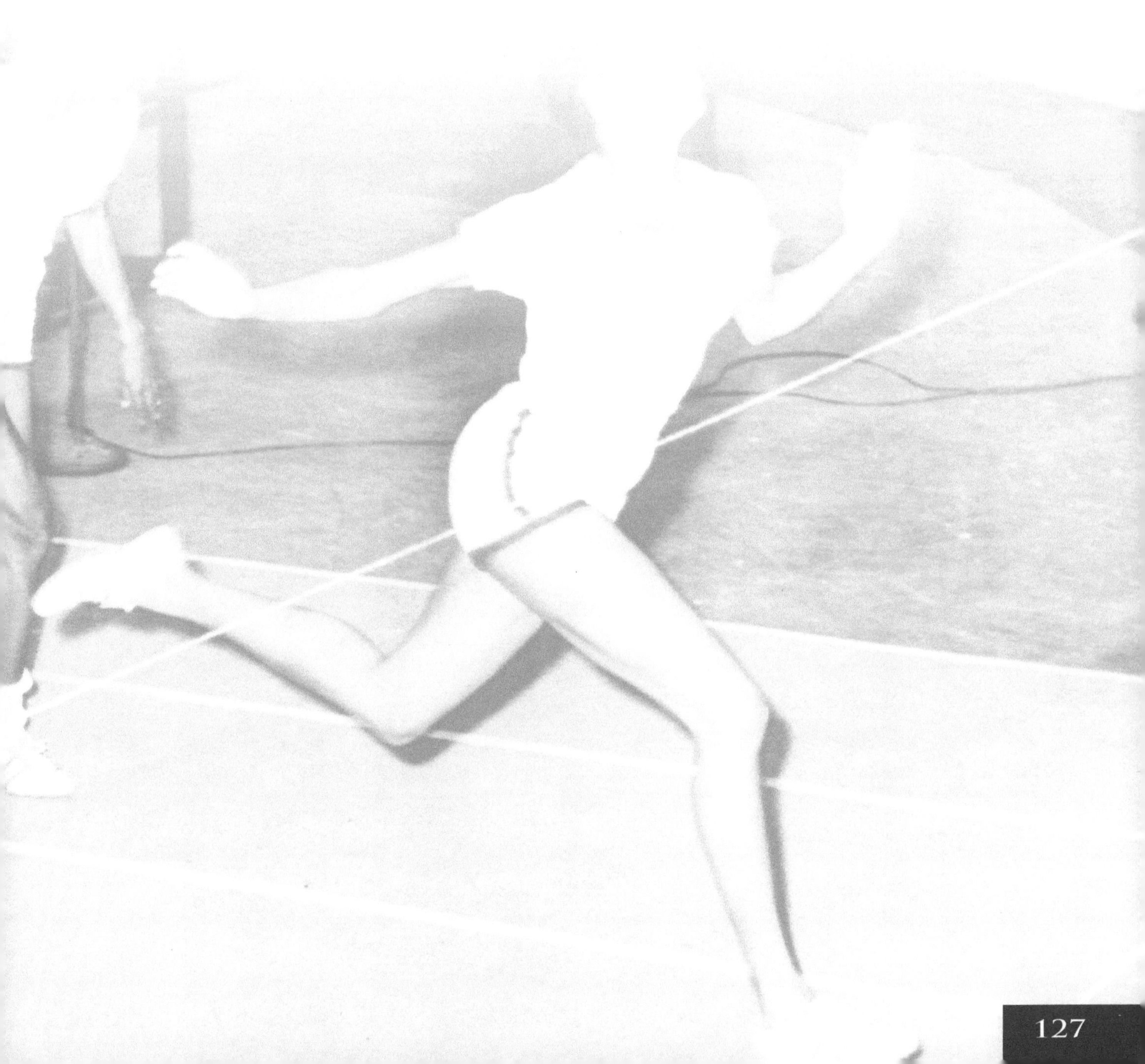

Think About It
THE SWORD

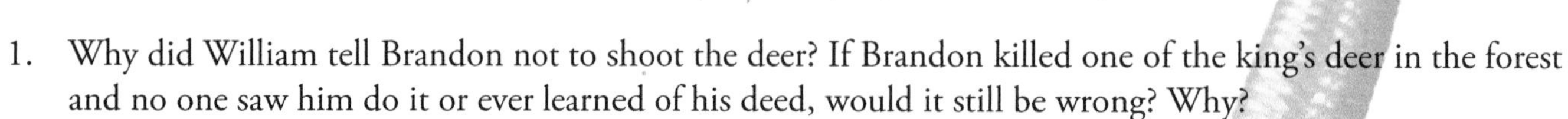

1. Why did William tell Brandon not to shoot the deer? If Brandon killed one of the king's deer in the forest and no one saw him do it or ever learned of his deed, would it still be wrong? Why?

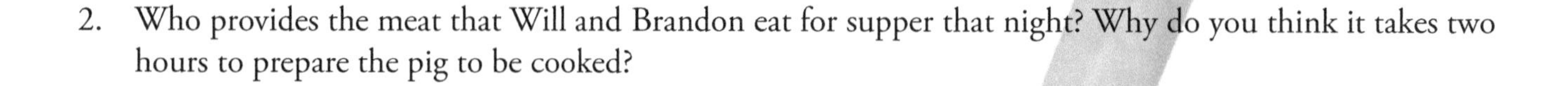

2. Who provides the meat that Will and Brandon eat for supper that night? Why do you think it takes two hours to prepare the pig to be cooked?

3. Why have William and Brandon been in the forest for the past week? Have they been successful? Why does William think they've had trouble tracking the wolf?

4. Although he clearly knows right from wrong, why does Brandon sometimes have trouble choosing to do the right thing?

5. Read Zechariah 4:10. How does this verse apply to the story of David the shepherd boy? How does it apply to Brandon's life?

6. Why do you suppose William changed his mind about becoming a priest? Can he serve God just as well by being a knight? How?

7. Why is William never without his sword outside the castle walls?

8. The apostle Paul calls the Bible "the Sword of the Spirit" (Ephesians 6:17). How is the Bible like a sword? How can knowing the Word of God protect you?

Nature's Footprints

Read a book about tracking animals, then plan a nature hike with a parent. Bring equipment to draw or photograph any animal prints you find. Record your findings here.

Words to Know

TRUST

SPIRITUAL DISCIPLINE

SELF-CONTROL

HIDE IT IN MY HEART

Write your favorite translation of the verse below and memorize it.

BUT THOSE WHO TRUST IN THE LORD WILL FIND NEW STRENGTH. THEY WILL SOAR HIGH ON WINGS LIKE EAGLES. THEY WILL RUN AND NOT GROW WEARY. THEY WILL WALK AND NOT FAINT.

ISAIAH 40:31, NLT

Make a Note of It
CHRIST IS MY COVERING

Athletes wear the colors of the teams and countries they represent. When people meet you, can they immediately identify you as a Christian? How can you wear Christ's "colors"? List as many ways as you can think of to speak, behave, and dress in a manner that clearly and accurately shows Jesus to the world.

EYES ON THE PRIZE

```
O N W I N G S L I K E E A G L E S C J J
A Y X B T C O M M I T M E N T D W Q O A
P W G I G E Y E S O N T H E P R I Z E W
R P O V E K V Q I E N T H U S I A S M B
I S P I R I T U A L D I S C I P L I N E
O K I C N R A C E T U R W B W W N D D P
R R I T T W O B E T N U Y G W I S P E J
I E H O R W L B R P I N R L E T S H T S
T P A R A I Y V R O F W H C N H T E E T
I R G S I N M C E S O I A V D P R X R A
E E U C N N P H E T R T P H U Q A E M Y
S S V R I I I A X A M H G Q R S T R I O
Q E A O N N C M K M C P Z V A P E C N N
F N B W G G S P E I I U C Q N Z G I A C
I T O N Y P S I K N P R S Z C Z Y S T O
J C T R U S T O G A Q P X R E Y F E I U
F M B L K E L N Q W Z O F N E K J J O R
L E A R N F R O M M I S T A K E S W N S
G P P Q B E L I E V E E C H G J Q Q Z E
D W P I U F O S E L F C O N T R O L L V
```

endurance
victor's crown
Olympics
spiritual discipline
stamina
self-control
exercise
priorities
run with purpose
uniform
represent
race
training
eyes on the prize
winning
strategy
determination
believe
trust
on wings like eagles
champion
stay on course
learn from mistakes
commitment
enthusiasm

LIVING OUT LOUD

Make a Note of It
IF WE TRULY BELIEVED

Read John 14:11–13. What would the world be like if all the people in Christ's church truly believed God's promises? What kinds of things would you expect to see when you walk into a church on Sunday or any other day of the week? How might unbelievers react if they saw God's people doing "greater things" than Jesus did? How would your own home be different if you really believed God's promises?

Mini Book
GO FOR THE WIN!

Find the instructions on page 227.
Attach your finished mini book here.

Hide It in My Heart

Write your favorite translation of the verse below and memorize it.

Be self-controlled and alert. Your enemy the devil prowls around like a roaring lion looking for someone to devour. Resist him, standing firm in the faith.

1 Peter 5:8–9

My Prayer

Praise Report

I Spy

MEET SAGE

Based on what you've learned about Sage and her beliefs, draw a picture of her doing an everyday task. Or write a poem, story, or song about her or a conversation you might have with her.

Do You Remember?

1. Three countries have claimed Eric Liddell as their Olympic champion, but whom did Eric believe he represented?

2. If you are a Christian, what does God see when He looks at you?

3. In 1 Corinthians 9:24 (NLT), Paul writes, "Don't you realize that in a race everyone runs, but only one person gets the prize? So run to win!" Does he mean that Christians are competing against one another and that only one of us can win? If not, what does he mean?

4. Why did Wilma Rudolph's mother believe that Wilma would walk when her doctors did not? What did Wilma's mother teach her about God?

5. Why did Peter begin to sink when he was walking on the water? What can you learn from this story and apply to your own life?

6. Why did George Mueller refuse to ever ask anyone for money or donations to care for the children of the orphanage?

7. What is a spiritual discipline? What are some of these disciplines?

8. How does the devil try to use your past mistakes against you?

9. How is obedience importance to running the race well?

10. Why do athletes need to exercise self-control? Why should you exercise self-control?

RUN TO WIN!

Word List

children
Esau
trust
spiritual discipline
self-control
Eric Liddell
Chariots of Fire
training
Wilma Rudolph
Peter
George Mueller
mustard seed
resolutions
Tom Landry
James Naismith
commanded
Apostle Paul
lapis lazuli
affirmations
feng shui
Renaissance fair
astrology

Across

1. Italian newspapers called her the Black Gazelle
3. Having complete confidence that God will always do everything He promises
7. The study of the stars to know the future
8. Jacob's brother, a skilled hunter
10. He said, "I press toward the goal for the prize of the upward call of God in Christ Jesus" (Philippians 3:14, NKJV)
11. He was the "other guy" who walked on water
13. Outdoor festival in which participants reenact an earlier European period, usually between the 14th and 16th centuries
15. An exercise that, done regularly, helps me to grow spiritually
16. Doing the right thing even when I don't feel like it
18. "Blessed is the man whose quiver is full of" them (Psalm 127:5)
19. Oscar-winning film about the Olympic track team from England
20. A list of statements read aloud every day to promote positive thinking
21. Chinese art of space design thought to maximize positive energy

Down

2. "If you have faith as small as" this, "nothing will be impossible for you" (Matthew 17:20)
4. He coached the Dallas Cowboys from a winless team into world champions
5. Millions make them every December 31
6. Sage wears a necklace made of this semi-precious stone to protect against headaches and sore throats
9. Man who cared for more than 18,000 children at his English orphanage
12. Scottish runner who was born and died in China
14. He invented basketball as an evangelistic tool
17. "Everyone who competes in the games goes into strict ________" (1 Corinthians 9:25)
18. "Be careful to do what the Lord your God has ________ you; do not turn aside to the right or to the left" (Deuteronomy 5:32)

WHAT'S THE DIFFERENCE?
NEW AGE

1. How is the way Sage lives different from the way you live? How are your lives similar?

2. Why do you suppose Sage's mother keeps trying new beliefs and religions? What do you think she is looking for? What would Sage and her mother think if they visited your church?

3. Why does Sage like Ruby so much? Why does she want to be like Ruby when she grows up?

4. What is astrology? How is it different from astronomy?

5. What is an "affirmation"? How does Sage's mother think affirmations can help them? Where is one place a Christian can always go to be "affirmed"?

6. Ruby tells Sage that God is not a person but that God and the universe are the same thing. How is this different from what the Bible tells us about God?

7. Ruby says people can find harmony only if they discover the part of God that lives within them. How is this different from what the Bible teaches us about how to find personal harmony? What does the Bible say about God living inside you?

8. Sage and her mother are vegetarians, which means they don't eat any meat or fish. This is because Sage's mother believes that killing any living thing, even an animal, is a crime. What does the Bible say about killing animals?

9. Why do you think people go to Renaissance fairs and festivals? What do they expect to see and do there?

10. How is the way Ruby teaches Sage to see herself different from the way you are learning to see yourself as a child of God?

Find Out More

Books

The Priest with Dirty Clothes by R. C. Sproul (ages 4–8)
Adam Raccoon and the Race to Victory Mountain by Glen Keane (ages 4–8)
Big Tracks, Little Tracks: Following Animal Prints by Millicent Selsam (ages 4–8)
Crinkleroot's Book of Animal Tracking by Jim Arnosky (ages 9–12)
Animal Tracks and Signs (National Geographic) by Jinny Johnson (teens)
Sports: From Ancient Olympics to the Super Bowl by Liz Miles (ages 9–12)
Wilma Unlimited: How Wilma Rudolph Became the World's Fastest Woman by Kathleen Krull and David Diaz (ages 4–12)
George Mueller: The Guardian of Bristol's Orphans by Geoff Benge and Janet Benge (ages 9–12)
The Wilderking Trilogy by Jonathan Rogers (ages 11–14)
The Black Arrow by Robert Louis Stevenson (ages 9–14)
The Pilgrim's Progress by John Bunyan (ages 12 and up)

Songs

"Stand Up, Stand Up for Jesus" by George Duffield, Jr.
"Joy in the Journey" by Michael Card
"I Can See Jesus in You" by Twila Paris
"Heart of a Champion" by Carman, Jimmy Santis, and Steve Skinner
"Running After You" by Mike Guglielmucci
"Live Like We're Dying" by Andrew Frampton, Stephen Kipner, Daniel O'Donoghue, and Mark Sheehan
"No Better Place" by Steven Curtis Chapman
"Love Is Always There" by Carolyn Arends
"Like a Child" by Dan Haseltine, Charlie Lowell, and Matt Odmark
"East to West" by Mark Hall and Bernie Herms
"Dear Shame" by Steve Taylor and Peter Furler

WHAT KIND OF FRUIT ARE YOU GROWING?

Think About It
The Challenge

1. According to the code of chivalry, what character traits will Brandon need to develop if he is to become a knight of the realm? Which of these traits does Brandon already demonstrate as a page to Sir William and a friend to Gwyneth?

2. According to Lady Maud, why must a good knight also be gentle?

3. Why is Quentin upset with Brandon and William? How does he express his anger toward them? How could he express his feelings in a healthier way?

4. What does Sir William teach Brandon about fear?

5. Before the twentieth century, the Holy Spirit was often called the Holy Ghost, and many people still use this name today. Who is the Holy Spirit? Where can you find Him? How can you know He's there?

6. What would it be like to visit the throne room of an earthly king? What kinds of things would you expect to see there?

7. What do you imagine it will it be like to stand before God's throne in heaven? What do you expect to see there? How do you think you will feel?

WORDS TO KNOW

FRUIT OF THE SPIRIT

HOLINESS

HIDE IT IN MY HEART

Write your favorite translation of the verse below and memorize it.

BUT THE FRUIT OF THE SPIRIT IS LOVE, JOY, PEACE, PATIENCE, KINDNESS, GOODNESS, FAITHFULNESS, GENTLENESS AND SELF-CONTROL. AGAINST SUCH THINGS THERE IS NO LAW.

GALATIANS 5:22–23

Make a Note of it
THE GOOD SAMARITAN

Read the story of the Good Samaritan in Luke 10:30–37. The Jewish people of Jesus' time did not like the people of Samaria, and the feeling was mutual. Yet in the story, the Good Samaritan put aside his personal feelings to do the right thing. How did the Samaritan show love and kindness to the Jewish man? Why do you think the Jewish priest and the Levite did not stop to help the man? Think of a person you do not like. How can you show love and kindness to that person?

AGAINST SUCH THINGS THERE IS NO LAW

I K T Y F R U I T O F T H E S P I R I T
M N J S G I Z U Q G G A R D E N I N G Y
G P X T H J Y W W W T O I F L T S R A T
Z R R D C O I Y E I K P P A O O A O R N
W W N U O Y T V E U N E A I V T G O B C
K A P U N K H G D Y A A R T E H U T D L
G T X L H I I Z S O K C A H X E A S R F
G D Z B R A N C H I P E B F I L R T D N
Y N X F V M R G N M J J L U K O O Q D N
O A M E F E Q U D D E N E L J N C K W G
R U T H A N D B O A Z W O N K E A M W E
P F T R U E V I N E E G F E G R C K Y N
M R A L P A T I E N C E T S O A T I I T
H S E L F C O N T R O L H S O N U M G L
O T S D K M B X U Q B U E C D G S J Q E
K I N D N E S S J A D F S T N E Q V Q N
O T O N T O K V Q M H Z O S E R X D Y E
H O L I N E S S F O A Z W J S Z J S W S
W V N G R O W T H N D Q E U S V D M R S
G B G E B J M R M J R V R K U D D E P E

Parable of the Sower
Fruit of the Spirit
love
joy
peace
patience
kindness
goodness
gentleness
faithfulness
self-control
holiness
The Lone Ranger
Tonto
Gandhi
Ruth and Boaz
gardening
True Vine
branch
saguaro cactus
pruning
roots
weeds
growth

Make a Note of It
THE BOAZ PRINCIPLE

Read chapter 2 from the book of Ruth. Had she come to another field, Ruth might have been harassed by the workers. Her life may even have been in danger. How does Boaz demonstrate gentleness, or "quiet strength," toward Ruth? How do you treat the new girl on the block? What about the boy who doesn't quite fit in with the other kids? Do you stand up for the girl who is being teased or bullied? If you see a small boy who has fallen off his bike, do you stop to help him? What do you think your gentleness and kindness might mean to these kids?

Make a Note of It
NURTURING YOUR FRUIT

Make a list of the fruit of the Spirit. Now talk with a parent to determine which of these are currently strongest in your life. Which ones need more water and work? How can you go about cultivating these attitudes in your life?

Mini Book
FRUIT OF THE SPIRIT

Find the instructions on page 231.
Attach your finished mini book here.

Hide It in My Heart

Write your favorite translation of the verse below and memorize it.

I am the Lord your God. Keep yourselves holy for me because I am holy.

Leviticus 11:44, ICB

My Prayer

PRAISE REPORT

I Spy

Meet Jin-Ho

Based on what you've learned about Jin-Ho and his beliefs, draw a picture of him doing an everyday task. Or write a poem, story, or song about him or a conversation you might have with him.

Do You Remember?

1. How can you know if you are becoming more like Christ?

2. What is God's definition of a productive Christian life?

3. How is all the fruit of the Spirit really an expression of love?

4. How is love more than an emotion? How was Jesus' earthly life the ultimate expression of love?

5. What does Colossians 3:12 say we, as Christians, should always wear? How can you be sure you're "spiritually dressed" for the day each day?

6. Mark Twain once wrote, "Always do right. This will gratify some people and astonish the rest." Why is this true?

7. What does it mean to be faithful? How can you demonstrate faithfulness in your home?

8. What does it mean that gentleness can be defined as "strength under control"?

9. What are some ways you can cultivate strong "roots" in your life?

10. Why is it important to get rid of the weeds in your life? What are some weeds you need to pull starting today?

HOW DOES YOUR GARDEN GROW?

Word List

Capernaum	The Lone Ranger	Jesus Christ
chivalry	loyal friends	pruning
St. George	Mohandas K. Gandhi	weed
Fruit of the Spirit	Boaz	holiness
love	listen	Pyongyang
good	gentle	juche
Good Samaritan	fruit	Mass Games
Robert Indiana	saguaro cactus	

Across

1. Purity in my heart in everything I think and say and do
5. Jin-Ho's home town
6. The cutting off of branches to shape the vine and stimulate new growth
8. The knights' code of conduct
10. Jesus said, "If any remain in me and I remain in them, they produce much _____" (John 15:5, NCV)
12. Tonto's pal
13. "Be quick to ______, slow to speak" (James 1:19)
16. Annual event at which tens of thousands of gymnasts and dancers perform the history of communist North Korea
17. He stopped to help the man who had been left for dead
19. He showed gentleness, or quiet strength, toward Ruth
20. The patron saint of England
21. He is the source of "living water" (John 4:10)
22. An unwanted plant that tends to overgrow or choke out more desirable plants

Down

2. "Many will say they are _____ ______, but who can find one who is truly reliable?" (Proverbs 20:6, NLT)
3. "As we have opportunity, let us do ____ to all people" (Galatians 6:10)
4. North Korean ideal of self-reliance
7. Christlike attitudes that show the Holy Spirit is working in my life
9. His LOVE sculpture became a cultural icon
11. He said, "In a gentle way, you can shake the world"
13. According to 1 Corinthians 13:8, it never fails
14. This Sonoran Desert plant can grow fifty feet tall
15. Seaside village where the apostle Peter lived
18. "A ______ answer turns away wrath, but a harsh word stirs up anger" (Proverbs 15:1)

What's the Difference?
COMMUNISM

1. How is the way Jin-Ho lives different from the way you live? How are your lives similar?

2. Why do you think Jin-Ho's father is so careful to wear his Great Leader political pin in public?

3. Kim Il-sung died in 1994, but the North Koreans still call him their "Eternal President." This has even been written into the country's constitution. Is Kim Il-sung truly eternal? Why or why not?

4. The communist worldview generally teaches that all people are equal and must share their resources equally. How is this different from the system of government where you live?

5. The president of North Korea is said to live in a seven-story palace while the average worker in his country earns less than $1,000 per year. Meanwhile, some government officials receive better food and greater benefits than the average citizen. Why do you think some citizens are treated as "more equal" than others under communist rule?

6. The North Korean ideal of *juche*, or self-reliance says that "mankind is the master of everything and decides everything." How does this compare to what the Bible teaches?

7. Some North Koreans believe their president has the ability to control the weather based on his mood. What would that be like, having the weather depend on the emotions of a human being? Who do you believe controls the weather?

8. Although the North Korean constitution permits religious freedom, the communist government promotes atheism—the belief that there is no God—and imposes strict control over the religious activities of its people. Possession of Bibles and other religious materials is reported to be illegal and may be punished by imprisonment or even execution. What would you do if your country's government said you could no longer worship God or tell others about Jesus? Why?

Find Out More

Books

9 Fruits Alive by Mindy MacDonald (ages 4–8)
Kids' Travel Guide to the Fruits of the Spirit by Group Publishing (ages 6–11)
Fruit of the Spirit by David Walters and Daniel Henigman (ages 9–14)
Saint George and the Dragon by Margaret Hodges and Trina Schart Hyman (ages 9–12)
Parzival: The Quest of the Grail Knight by Katherine Paterson (ages 9–14)
Men of Iron by Howard Pyle (ages 11–14)
Adam of the Road by Elizabeth Janet Gray (ages 11–14)
St. George for England by G. A. Henty (ages 11–16)
Who Put Lemons in My Fruit of the Spirit? by Martha Bolton (teens)

Songs

"I Can Only Imagine" by Bart Millard
"All Hail the Power of Jesus' Name" by Edward Perronet and John Rippon
"Crown Him with Many Crowns" by Matthew Bridges and Godfrey Thring
"Come Thou Fount" by Robert Robinson
"Trading My Sorrows" by Darrell Evans
"Mourning into Dancing" by Tommy Walker
"In the Garden" by C. Austin Miles
"Seeds" by Kathy Mattea
"Whom Shall I Fear" by Darrel Evans

WHO DO YOU THINK YOU ARE?

Think About It
The Ceremony

1. What is a vigil? Why is this an important part of William's preparation for the knighting ceremony? Research to learn the symbolism of what William is wearing for his vigil.

2. Why do you think Quentin takes William's sword?

3. Why is Brandon so determined to get the sword back in time for the ceremony?

4. Where does Brandon get his idea for chasing away the wolf? Looking back over Brandon's adventures, how is young Brandon like the biblical Gideon?

5. How does Quentin show the beginnings of humility after his rescue?

6. How does William answer wisely when the king asks if he will stand firm against the enemies of Christ?

7. How does the knight's sword remind him of his responsibilities?

8. Brandon has learned much about himself and his identity. How is his position as a child of God like his adoption as a child of the king of England? How might the king's revelation change Brandon's thinking about himself and his future?

9. How are you like a knight in the service of the King of all kings?

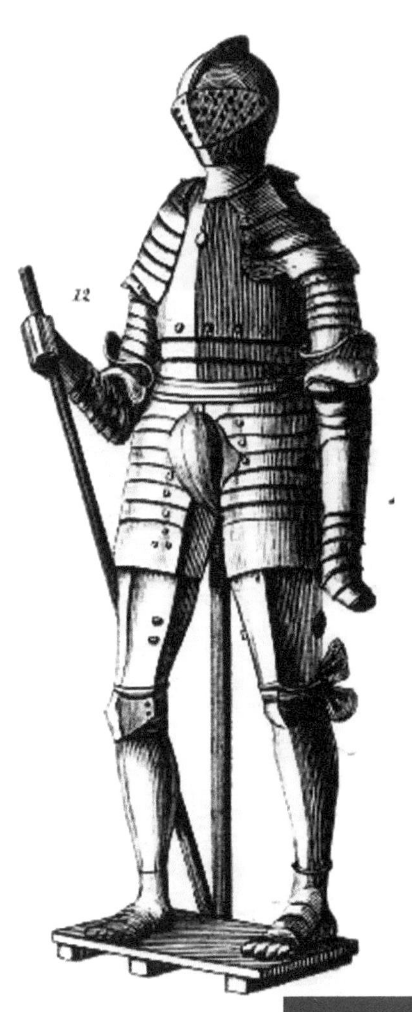

Words to Know

JUSTIFIED

SAINT

CHURCH

AMBASSADOR

Hide It in My Heart

Write your favorite translation of the verse below and memorize it.

THEREFORE, IF ANYONE IS IN CHRIST, HE IS A NEW CREATION; THE OLD HAS GONE, THE NEW HAS COME!

2 CORINTHIANS 5:17

Make a Note of It

What the Bible Says About Saint ________

Think of the Bible as a personal love letter from God to you. Insert your first name into each of the following verses and write them out: 2 Corinthians 5:17–19, Psalm 4:3, Romans 8:1, 2 Corinthians 7:1, Ephesians 3:12, 1 John 5:5, and 1 Peter 2:9. For example, "The Lord has set apart Kendra for himself " (Psalm 4:3).

WHO I AM IN CHRIST

Z E V E R Y T O N G U E C O N F E S S T
S A I N T Z U R A M B A S S A D O R T A
E V E R Y K N E E S H O U L D B O W B U
T Q L V B F T R A C P Q R E Y B X P O T
Y C K X J R X C G C X C I C B U I H O H
S R H G B P A F H F O F X Y Q H E S K O
E X O V E Z X N I U I N T U S X U W O R
T H L O Q R E E D T R S F D V O B M F I
A U Y V H G T Z S N I C R I I F O O L T
P P N G P E Y U G R E O H R D D M V I Y
A Y A T Y B J C H L L W O K E E H E F A
R D T K N D L C O R V T C E Z W N R E N
T K I W I W N B H H C B R R S A J C Q N
I W O I L I K M Z I E F R L E R X O E U
F L N P W X Q A V R M I E C F A V M V D
T H R O N E R O O M Q K R P B P T E V K
J E S U S C H R I S T I S L O R D I K Q
S U Y C I T I Z E N O F H E A V E N O F
L B U T T E R F L Y U A C C E S S G H N
S E T F R E E F R O M S I N Y W V X E P

co-heir
throne room
access
justified
saint
church

ambassador
brand-new creation
butterfly
citizen of heaven
Book of Life
holy nation

overcome
victorious
authority
lordship
every knee should bow
every tongue confess

Jesus Christ is Lord
set apart
set free from sin
freedom
confidence
in Christ

Make a Note of It

What Can God Do for Me?

Make a complete list of all the problems, large and small, that you or other family members are facing right now. Now put a checkmark next to all of the problems that are so big and terrible that Jesus' victory on the cross could not overcome them. Look at your list one more time and know that because Jesus has overcome the world, you do not need to worry or be afraid of any situation in your life.

MINI BOOK
YOU ARE SOMEONE NEW!

Find the instructions on page 237.
Attach your finished mini book here.

Hide It in My Heart

Write your favorite translation of the verse below and memorize it.

Therefore God exalted him to the highest place and gave him the name that is above every name, that at the name of Jesus every knee should bow, in heaven and on earth and under the earth, and every tongue confess that Jesus Christ is Lord, to the glory of God the Father.

Philippians 2:9–11

My Prayer

Praise Report

I Spy

QUARTERS ONLY
25¢
TO OPERATE
LONG RANGE BINOCULARS
1. DROP COIN IN SLOT
2. PULL HANDLE DOWN
ALL THE WAY-LET GO
3. TO CLEAR VISION - TURN RED KNOB

Meet Mei

Based on what you've learned about Mei and her beliefs, draw a picture of her doing an everyday task. Or write a poem, story, or song about her or a conversation you might have with her.

Do You Remember?

1. Why are so many people today unhappy with their lives? What do they do to try to fill their need for God?

2. Instead of looking in the mirror, where should you be looking to understand your true worth as a person?

3. What does the name "Christian" mean? Why have you been given this new name?

4. How is your transformation into a new creation like that of a caterpillar turning into a butterfly?

5. If you think of yourself as a loser, how will you act? If you think of yourself as a new creation and child of the Most High God, how will you act?

6. What does it mean to be justified in Christ?

7. What does it mean to be a saint? How should you live because the Lord has set you apart for Himself?

8. The word "church" comes from the Greek word *ekklesia*. What does the word *ekklesia* mean? Who or what is the church?

9. What are your responsibilities as an ambassador of Christ?

10. Why is it important to remember that Jesus has "overcome the world" (John 16:33)? What has He given you the authority to do?

VICTORY IN CHRIST

Word List

Strider	condemnation	blameless
Peter and the Wolf	citizen	ambassador
Joan of Arc	church	authority
Gideon	Book of Life	Tianjin
Christian	heaven	persecution
in Christ	Seabiscuit	Shangdi
justified	Nike	house church
saint	overcome	witnesses

Across

3. Christ has been given "all _________ on heaven and on earth" (Matthew 28:18)
4. "_________ evil with good" (Romans 12:21)
6. "No good thing does he withhold from those whose walk is __________" (Psalm 84:11)
7. Appointed representative of a nation
9. The family of God, with Christ as its head
10. Knobby-kneed grandson of Man o' War
11. "Therefore, if anyone is __ _____ he is a new creation" (2 Corinthians 5:17)
13. A Chinese name for God meaning "Emperor Above"
15. "Therefore, there is now no _____________ for those who are in Christ Jesus" (Romans 8:1)
16. Mei's home town
18. This name means "follower of Christ"
20. His biblical victory in battle inspired Brandon
21. Prokofiev's gift to the children of Moscow
22. A person who has been justified through faith in Jesus Christ
23. Aragorn's alias

Down

1. Her leadership inspired the French troops
2. A small group of believers that usually meets in individuals' homes
5. Mistreatment of an individual or group by a government
8. Declared innocent or free from guilt
12. "And you will be my _________, telling people about me everywhere . . . to the ends of the earth" (Acts 1:8, NLT)
14. The name of every child of God is written here
15. A resident or member of a particular city, state, or country
17. Greek goddess of victory
19. The true home of every child of God

WHAT'S THE DIFFERENCE? CHRISTIANITY

1. How is the way Mei lives different from the way you live? How are your lives similar?

2. Why are male babies valued more than female babies by Chinese families? What potential problems can you see arising from China's "one child" policy?

3. What is persecution? Why does the Chinese government persecute its citizens who follow Jesus?

4. Why do you think a communist government might consider Christianity to be dangerous?

5. Why do Chinese families clean their homes thoroughly for the new year? Why does Mei's mother say she cleans her house?

6. How is Mei's church different from yours? How is it similar?

7. Is a church that meets in someone's home still a church? Why?

8. Why is prayer so important to the people in Mei's church?

9. How has persecution of the church affected Mei's faith? How would it affect yours?

Find Out More

Books

A Medieval Feast by Aliki (ages 4–8)
Adam Raccoon and the King's Big Dinner by Glen Keane (ages 4–8)
The Squire and the Scroll by Jennie Bishop and Preston McDaniels (ages 4–8)
Come on, Seabiscuit! by Ralph Moody (ages 6–14)
The Kingdom Series by Chuck Black (ages 12 and up)
The Knights of Arrethtrae series by Chuck Black (ages 12 and up)
Do Hard Things: A Teenage Rebellion Against Low Expectations by Alex and Brett Harris (teens)

Songs

"Free to Be Me" by Francesca Battistelli
"Getting Into You" by Matt Thiessen
"Here I Am (Send Me Out)" by Michael Bleecker
"Until the Whole World Hears" by Roger Glidewell, Mark Hall, Bernie Herms, and Jason McArthur
"Lord, Reign in Me" by Brenton Brown
"Ancient of Days" by Gary Sadler and Jamie Harvill
"I Am a Friend of God" by Michael Gungor and Israel Houghton

LESSON 1 WORD SEARCH
THERE'S NO GOD LIKE MINE!

J E O M N I P O T E N T E T O F C K L T
Q I K L K F J Z V M A M E Z P S H O U J
T F M O M N I S C I E N T I O E R C S X
P L N A P G V Z W Z P M G K M C I X P T
E B Q S G S U I A W M B O F N R S U K X
R Y M Y K E H H N T I R D H I E T N Q I
S L H V V V H U C G V V S W P T L C W M
O X O N D F I T Y I X V M O R I I C Z A
N F L J A Q Z Z U H F A A K E D K J Z G
C Y Y T V R U S S I A L S E S E E E G E
W O R L D V I E W E A U T E E N P C D B
S K Y H K N W V L E S A E T N T S T M E
U U Z S V U F B L H A B R E T I O R Q A
P O R M V H A B P H N L P R O T C M M R
E T B S L T A A S M P E I N K Y G T Y E
R T Z H U R S A C R I I E A G K A T A R
M I J M A N S O E Y U A C L R R H T T P
A Z M P T F Q R W N O X E C R W I R B A
N I H A E N O R M A N R O C K W E L L Q
L Q A T I S N M I R R O R Y R H X E W P

LESSON 2 WORD SEARCH
WHOSE GLORY?

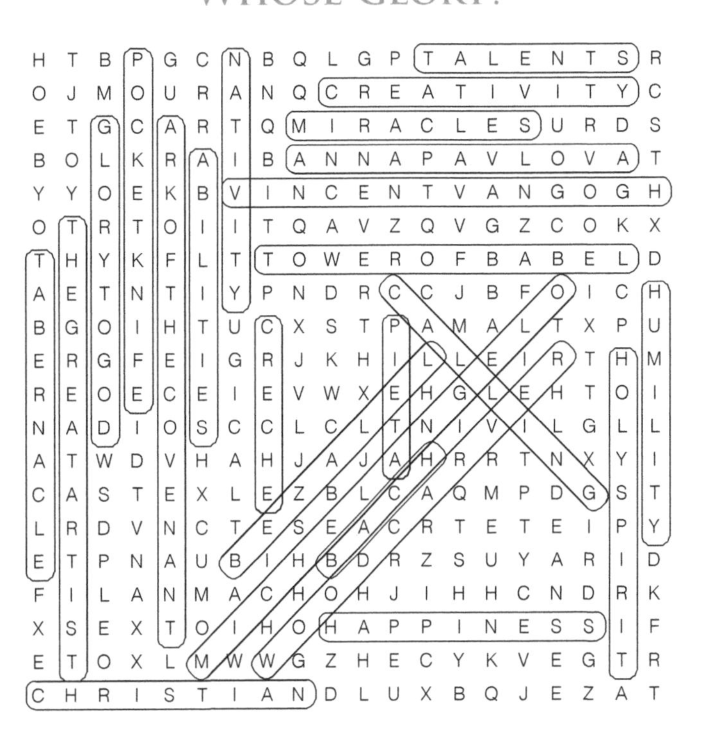

LESSON 3 WORD SEARCH
THINK ON THESE THINGS

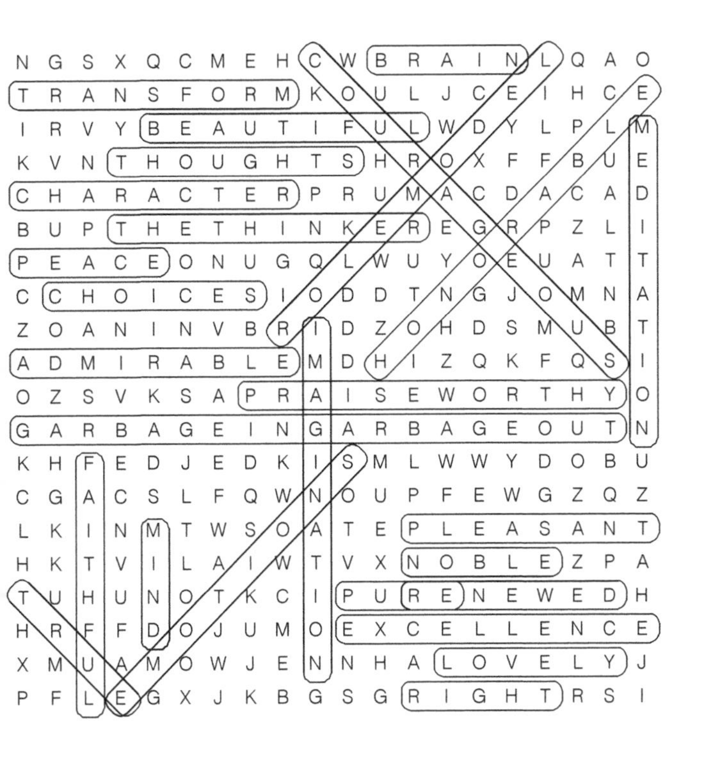

LESSON 4 WORD SEARCH
ONCE MORE . . . WITH FEELING

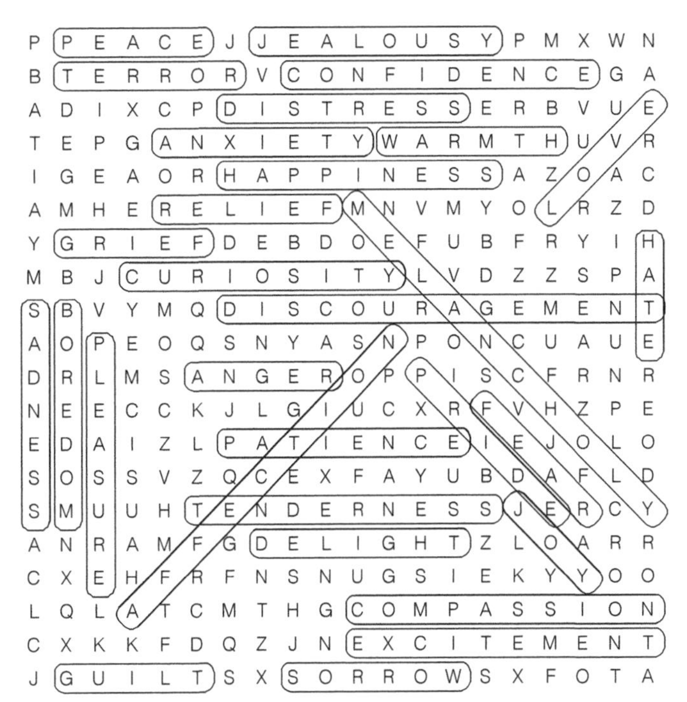

LESSON 5 WORD SEARCH
DECISIONS, DECISIONS

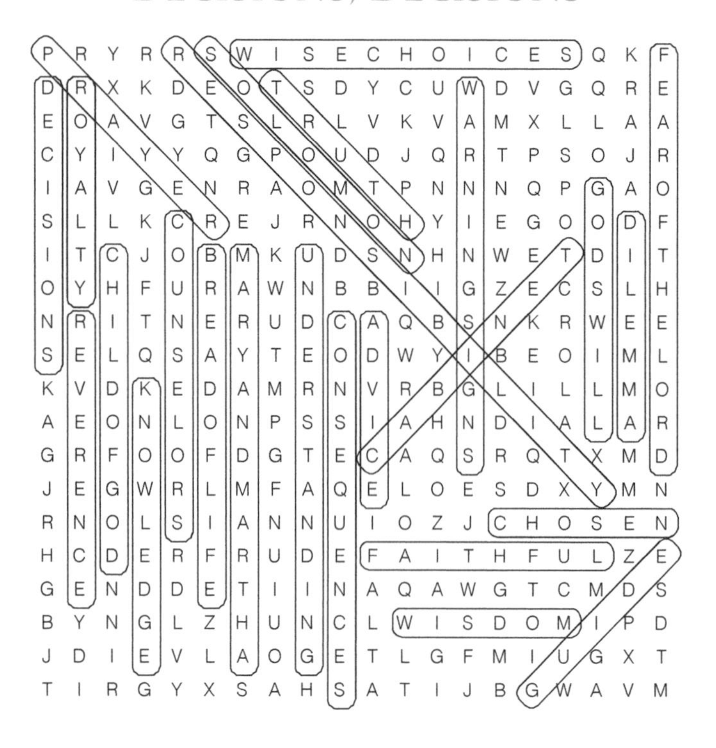

LESSON 6 WORD SEARCH
EYES ON THE PRIZE

```
O N W I N G S L I K E E A G L E S C J J
A Y X B T C O M M I T M E N T D W Q O A
P W G I G E Y E S O N T H E P R I Z E W
R P O V E K V Q I E N T H U S I A S M B
I S P I R I T U A L D I S C I P L I N E
O K I C N R A C E T U R W B W W N D D P
R R I T T W O B E T N U Y G W I S P E J
I E H O R W L B R P I N R L E T S H T S
T P A R A I Y V R O F W H C N H T E E T
I R G S I N M C E S O I A V D P R X R A
E E U C N N P H E T R T P H U Q A E M Y
S S V R I I I A X A M H G Q R S T R I O
Q E A O N N C M K M C P Z V A P E C N N
F N B W G G S P E I I U C Q N Z G I A C
I T O N Y P S I K N P R S Z C Z Y S T O
J C T R U S T O G A Q P X R E Y F E I U
F M B L K E L N Q W Z O F N E K J J O R
L E A R N F R O M M I S T A K E S W N S
G P P Q B E L I E V E E C H G J Q Q Z E
D W P I U F O S E L F C O N T R O L L V
```

LESSON 7 WORD SEARCH
AGAINST SUCH THINGS THERE IS NO LAW

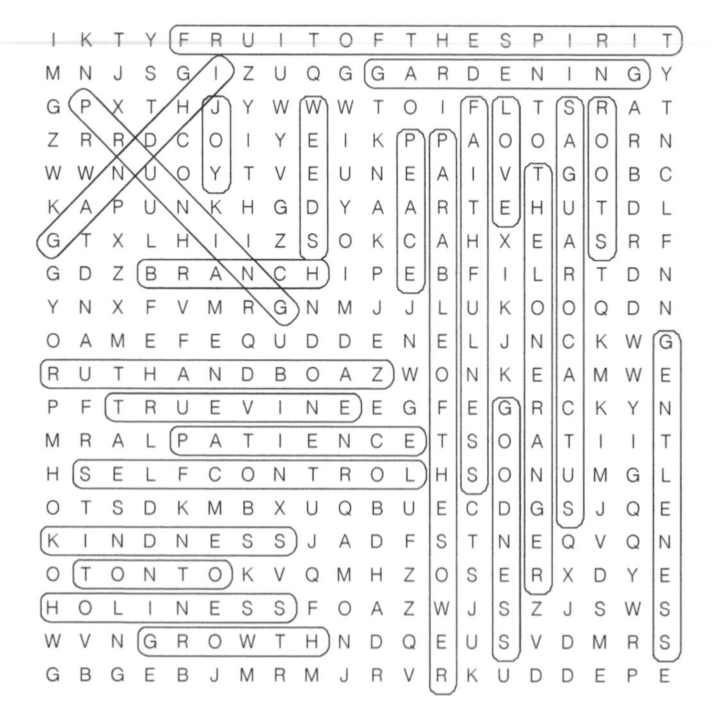

LESSON 8 WORD SEARCH
WHO I AM IN CHRIST

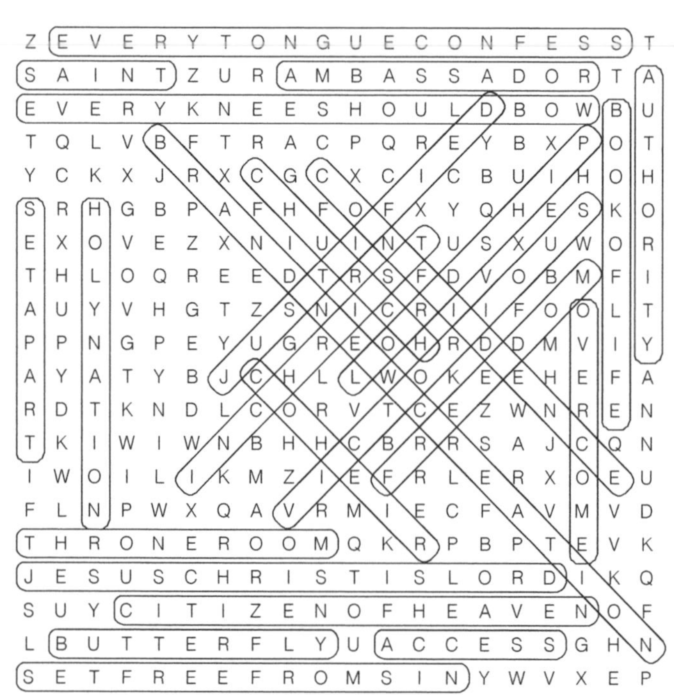

LESSON 1 CROSSWORD
GOD'S MASTERPIECE

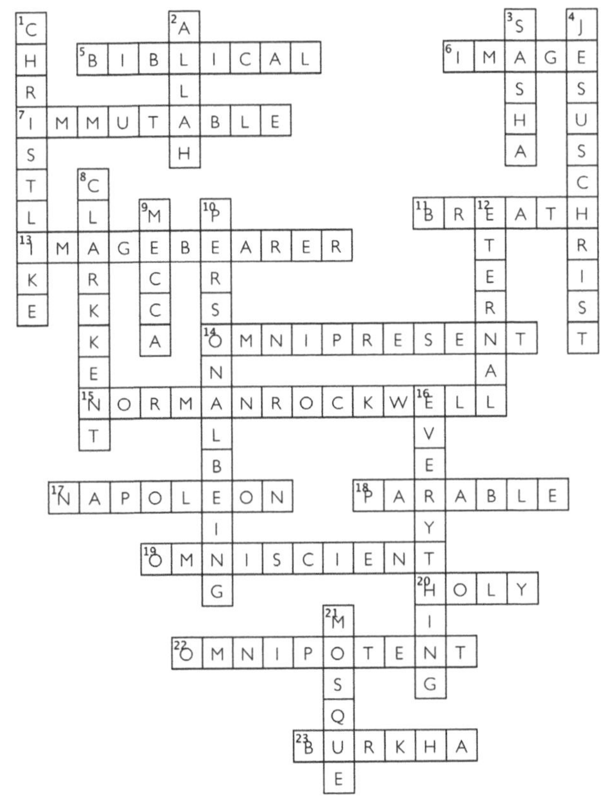

LESSON 2 CROSSWORD
UNIQUELY GIFTED TO GIVE GOD GLORY

LESSON 3 CROSSWORD
SOMETHING TO THINK ABOUT

LESSON 4 CROSSWORD
LET WISDOM BE YOUR GUIDE

LESSON 5 CROSSWORD

I'M A CHILD OF THE KING!

LESSON 6 WORD SEARCH

RUN TO WIN!

LESSON 7 CROSSWORD

HOW DOES YOUR GARDEN GROW?

LESSON 8 CROSSWORD

VICTORY IN CHRIST

LESSON 1

Instructions

1. Cut out the "Made in God's Image" pocket. Do not cut on the gold fold lines.
2. Fold the pocket tabs back. Apply glue where indicated and glue to page 19 in your journal.
3. Cut out each of the "God Is/Am I?" inserts. As you study each of the seven ways you are like or unlike God in lesson 1, write or draw the important points on the corresponding insert.
4. Use a hole punch to make a hole at the bottom of each insert. Stack the inserts and put a brad through the holes to hold them together.
5. Store the inserts in the "Made in God's Image" pocket in your journal.

GOD IS IMMUTABLE

Am I immutable?

GOD IS OMNIPRESENT

Am I omnipresent?

GOD IS OMNIPOTENT

Am I omnipotent?

GOD IS OMNISCIENT

Am I omniscient?

GOD IS HOLY

Am I holy?

LESSON 2

Instructions

1. Cut out each of the circles on this and the next two pages. Do not cut on the gold fold lines.
2. Fold each circle along the gold fold lines into halves with the "glue" instructions facing out.
3. Apply glue on the backs of the circles and attach each letter to its match.
4. Open each of the circles and write what you've learned about how God prepares us to be creative for His glory.
5. Apply glue to the end pieces where indicated and attach to page 44.

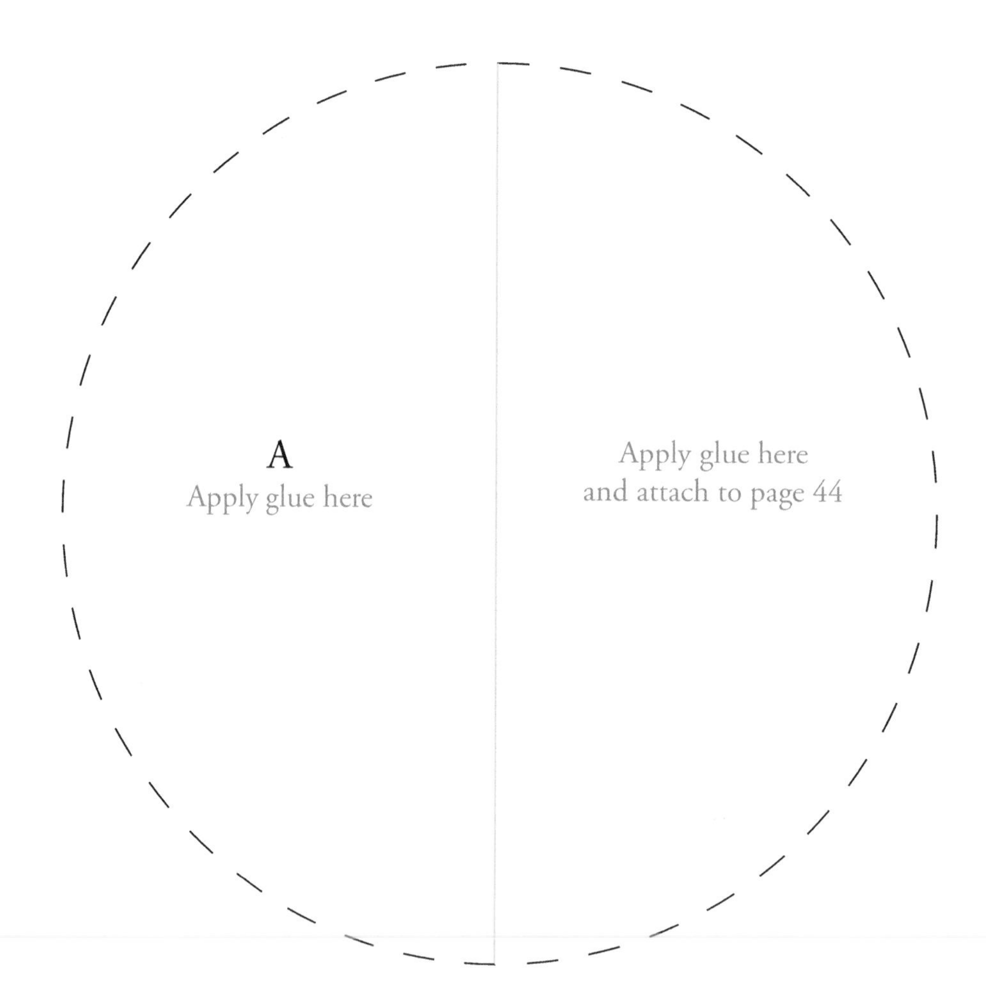
A
Apply glue here
Apply glue here
and attach to page 44

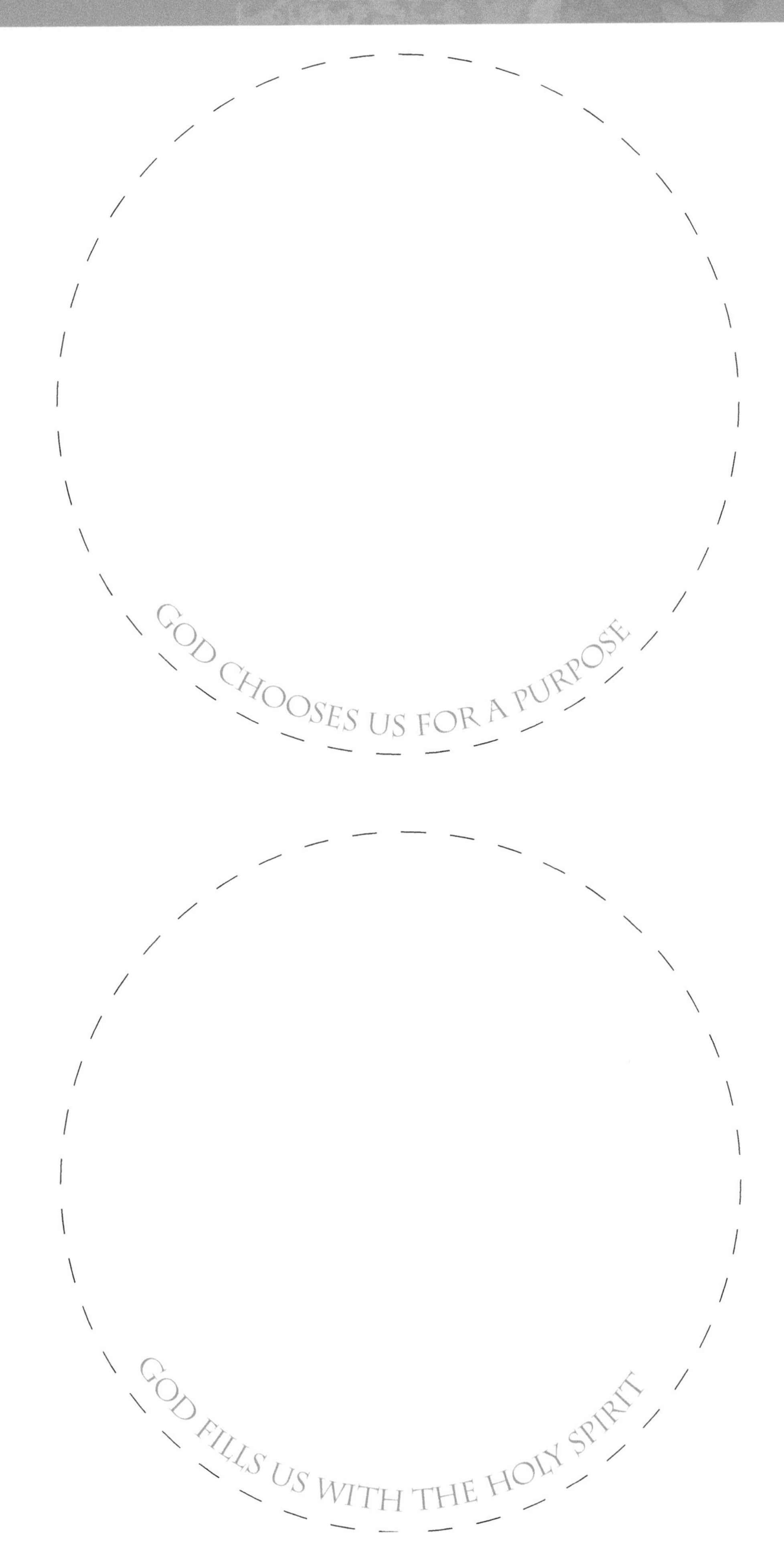
GOD CHOOSES US FOR A PURPOSE
GOD FILLS US WITH THE HOLY SPIRIT

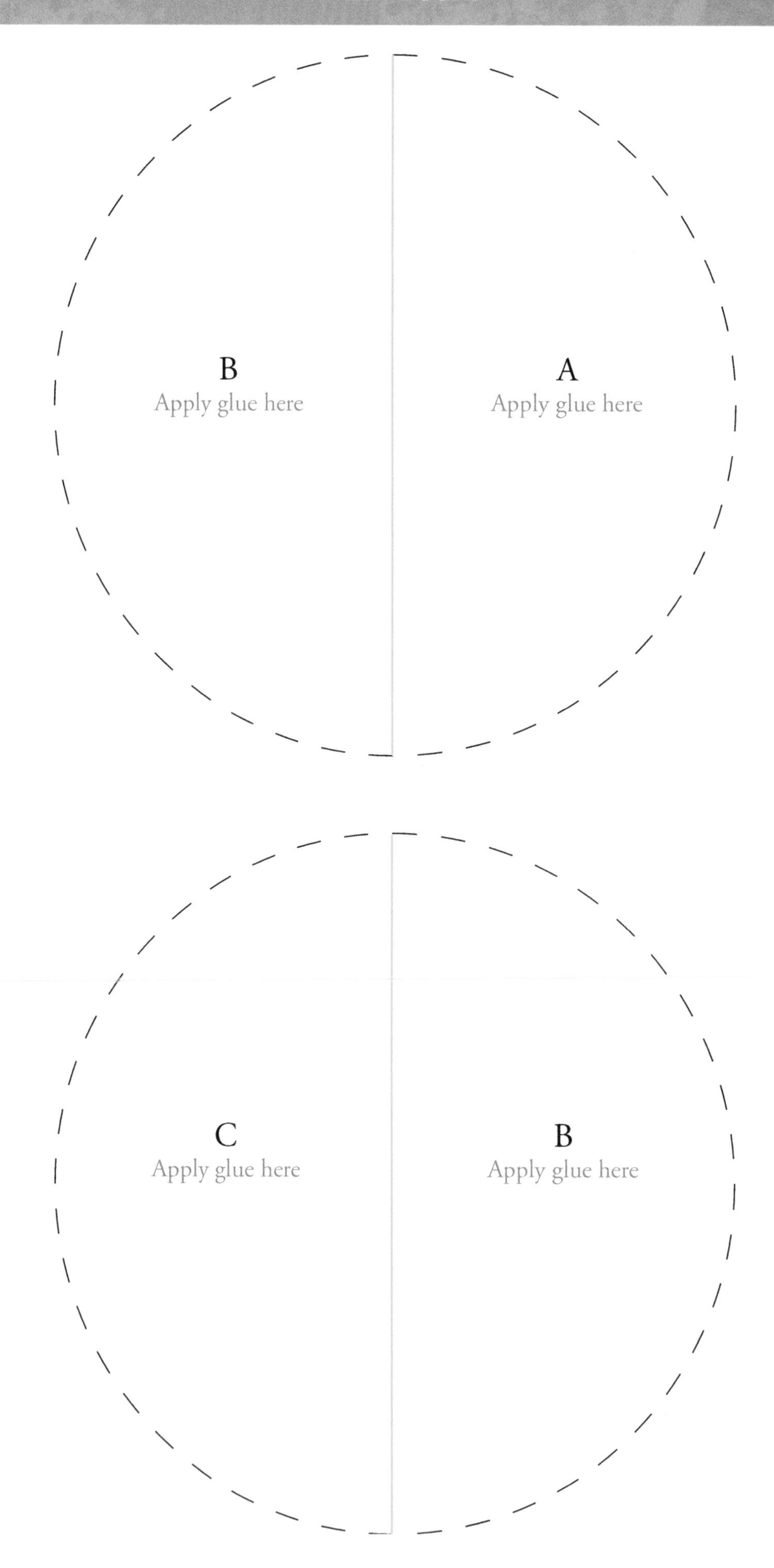
B
Apply glue here
A
Apply glue here
C
Apply glue here
B
Apply glue here

GOD GIVES US SPECIAL SKILLS AND ABILITIES
WHOSE GLORY?

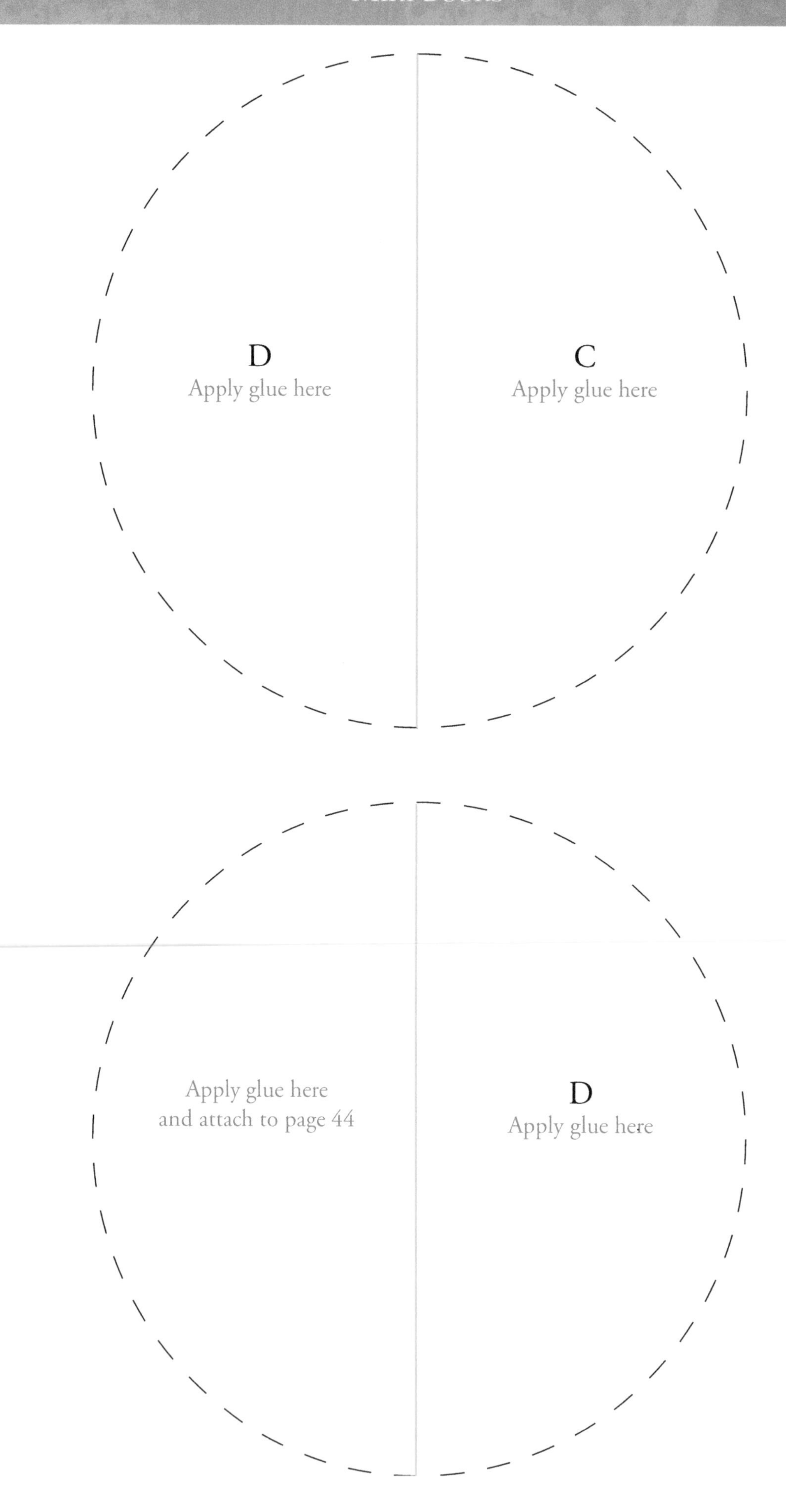
D
Apply glue here
C
Apply glue here
Apply glue here
and attach to page 44
D
Apply glue here

LESSON 3

Instructions

1. Cut out the entire mini book along the dotted lines on this page and the next page. Do not cut along the gold fold lines.
2. Stack the insert pages inside the cover and fold along the gold fold lines.
3. Open the book and staple it along the center.
4. As you study each of the six things to think about and one thing not to dwell upon, write or draw the important points on the corresponding mini book page.
5. Apply glue to the back of the book and attach it to page 67 in your journal.

Apply glue here
and attach to page 67 of your journal

SIX IN
ONE OUT

DON'T DWELL
ON THE NEGATIVE

7

THINK ABOUT
WHATEVER IS TRUE

1

THINK ABOUT
WHATEVER IS NOBLE

2

THINK ABOUT
WHATEVER IS ADMIRABLE

6

THINK ABOUT
WHATEVER IS RIGHT

3

THINK ABOUT
WHATEVER IS PURE

4

THINK ABOUT
WHATEVER IS LOVELY

5

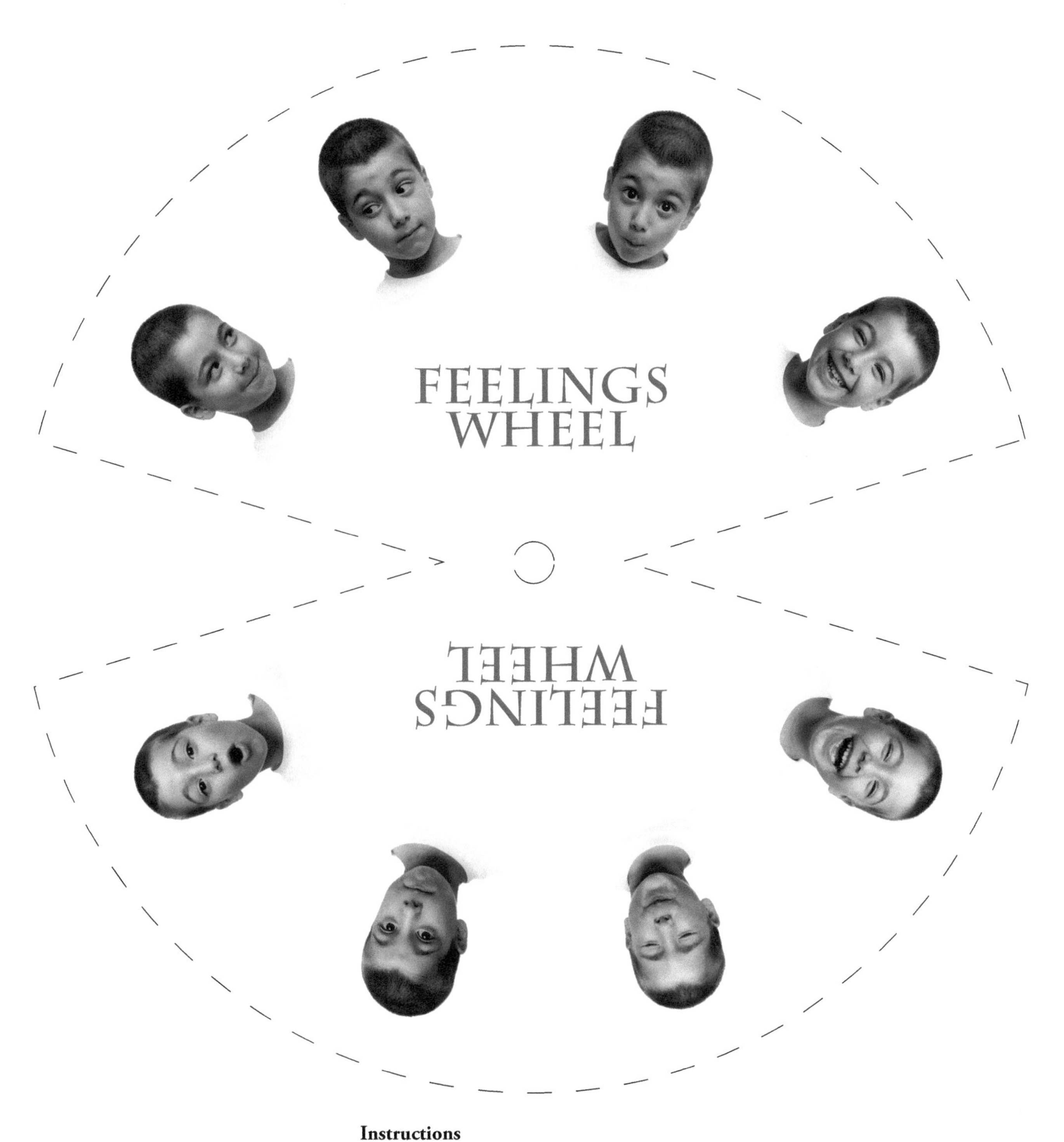

LESSON 4

Instructions

1. Cut out the "Feelings Wheel" at the top of this page and on the next page.
2. Stack the wheels on top of each other so the hole punch circles align. Use a hole punch to punch a hole in the center of both wheels.
3. Use a brad paper fastener to attach the top to the bottom.
4. As you study each of difficult emotions in lesson 4, write or draw the important points in the window that opens up when you move the wheel. Extra space has been provided for you to make notes on other feelings as well.
5. Apply glue to the back of the wheel and attach it to page 92 in your journal.

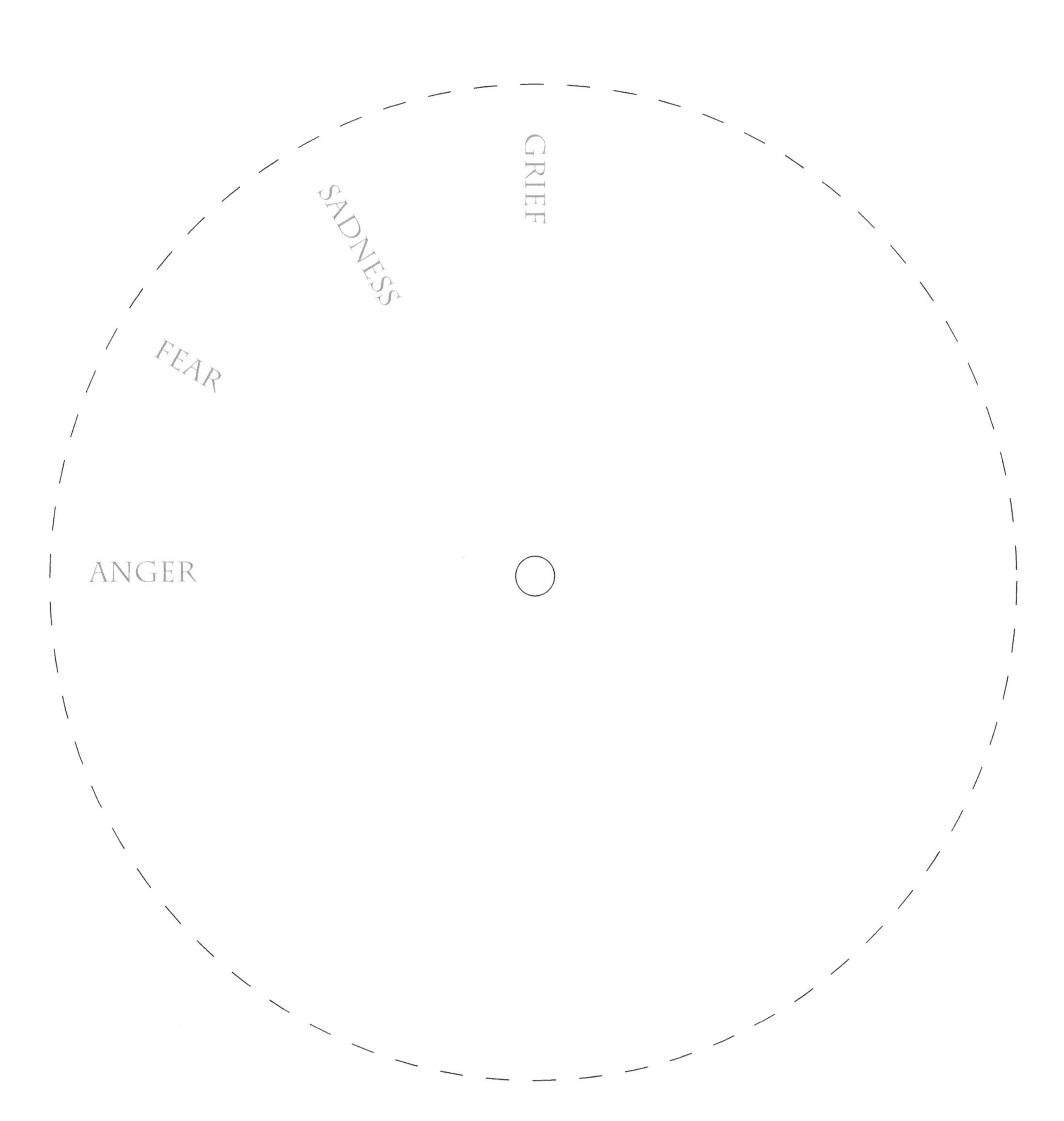
GRIEF
SADNESS
FEAR
ANGER

Apply glue here and attach to page 92 of your journal

LESSON 5

Instructions

1. Cut out the entire mini book along the dotted lines on this page and the next page. Do not cut along the gold fold lines.
2. Stack pages in order and staple the center of the book where indicated.
3. As you study each of the topics in lesson 5, write or draw the important points on the provided page.
4. Apply glue to the back of the book and attach it to page 114 in your journal.

Apply glue here and
attach to page 114 of your journal

CHOOSE

10

MAKE WRONG CHOICES?

3

WHY DO PEOPLE

2

CHRIST

11

ASK GOD

4

WISE COUNSEL

9

SEEK FIRST

8

5

LISTEN TO THE HOLY SPIRIT

6

7

LESSON 6

Instructions

1. Cut out the mini books along the dotted lines on this page and the next page. Do not cut along the gold fold lines. Fold each book along the gold fold lines.
2. As you study each of the topics in lesson 6, write or draw the important points inside the mini books.
3. Apply glue to the back of the books and attach them to page 140 in your journal.

Apply glue here
and attach to page 140

Apply glue here
and attach to page 140

BELIEVE
THAT GOD
KEEPS
HIS PROMISES

Apply glue here
and attach to page 140

Apply glue here
and attach to page 140

Apply glue here
and attach to page 140

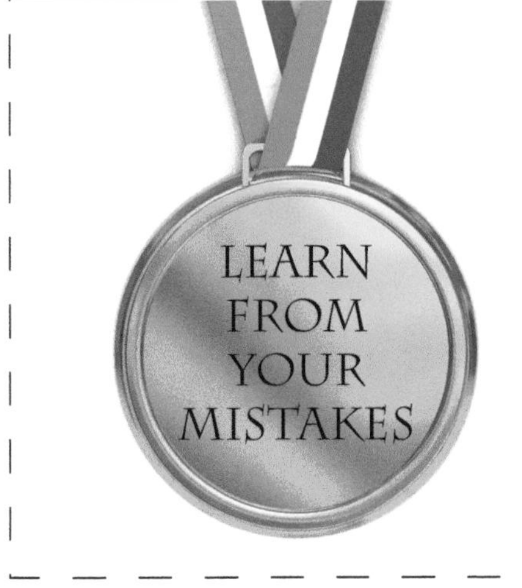

KEEP YOUR EYES
ON THE PRIZE

LESSON 7

Instructions

1. Cut out the basket.
2. Cut a slot in the center of the basket along the black dashed line.
3. Put glue along the back of the basket along the outer edges, being certain not to get any glue in the center.
4. Glue the basket to page 164.
5. Cut out the fruits on the next two pages.
6. Choose a type of fruit to represent each of the fruits of the Spirit. Write down what you learn on the back of each fruit.
7. Insert the fruits into the basket inside the slot. Pull the fruits out whenever you want to read about the fruit of the Spirit!

Apply glue here-Apply glue here-Apply glue here- Apply glue here-Apply glue here-Apply glue here

Apply glue here

DO NOT GLUE THIS SHADED AREA

Only Apply glue around edge of basket

Only Apply glue around edge of basket

Only Apply glue around edge of basket

YOU ARE A CITIZEN OF HEAVEN

YOU ARE A MEMBER OF GOD'S FAMILY

LESSON 8

Instructions

1. Cut out large rectangle on this page along the dotted lines. Don't cut the gold fold lines.
2. Fold the colored rectangles away from you along the gold fold lines.
3. Cut between the colored rectangles along the dotted lines.
4. Write what you learn about being someone new in lesson 8 under each flap.
5. Glue this side to page 188.

Apply Glue Here and attach to page 187 of your journal

YOU ARE JUSTIFIED

YOU ARE A SAINT

Paste your photo here.

ABOUT THE AUTHOR

WHAT PEOPLE ARE SAYING ABOUT ME AND MY BOOK

WHAT PEOPLE ARE SAYING ABOUT ME AND MY BOOK

WHAT PEOPLE ARE SAYING ABOUT ME AND MY BOOK

WHAT PEOPLE ARE SAYING ABOUT ME AND MY BOOK

WHAT PEOPLE ARE SAYING ABOUT ME AND MY BOOK

WHAT PEOPLE ARE SAYING ABOUT ME AND MY BOOK

WHAT PEOPLE ARE SAYING ABOUT ME AND MY BOOK

WHAT PEOPLE ARE SAYING ABOUT ME AND MY BOOK

Image License Information

Creative Commons Attribution 3.0 License
Forest & Kim Starr, 10

Creative Commons Attribution-ShareAlike 3.0 Unported (CC BY-SA 3.0)
Takkk, 44, 47
4028mdk09, 84
Holger.Ellgaard, 95
Natubico, 153
Dcrjsr, 198–199
FoeNyx, 233
Alvesgaspar, 233
Benjamint444, edited by Fir0002, 235

Creative Commons Attribution-ShareAlike 2.0 Unported (CC-BY-SA-2.0)
Don from Murfreesboro, TN, 78
Arwen Abendstem, 81
John Kratz from Burlington NJ, USA, 96
Joe Crawford from Moorpark, California, USA, 104
dbking, 105, 223
Trevor Rickard, 106
Sembazuru, 117
Rama, 130
Westside Shooter, 138
willconley777, 191

Creative Commons Attribution 2.0 Generic (CC BY 2.0)
Juan Rubiano, 11
Omar Chatriwala, 30
Andres Rueda, 65
Kapungo, 72
D. Sharon Pruitt from Hill Air Force Base, Utah, USA, 82
Dalbera, 119
JerryFeist, 128
Duncan Lilly, 132–133
The National Guard, 140
caddy_corner, 142
laffy4k, 143
Ali Smiles, 144
Brenda-Starr, 145
Philo Nordlund, 148
Horia Varlan, 144
Adam Jones, Ph.D., 157
Christopher Craig, 163
Lel4nd, 166
alancleaver_2000, 167
Peanuttt, 171
Gilad Rom from Israel, 174-175
US Fish & Wildlife Service -NE Region, 179
Horia Varlan, 152, 195
Georgio, 193
nSeika, 200
Jason Gulledge, 233
Abhijit Tembhekar, 233

Creative Commons ShareAlike 1.0
Cookiecaper, 102–103

GNU Free Documentation License
Terence Ong, 20
Arie M. den Toom, 25
PJ, 43
Nino Barbieri, 71
Cancre, 76
Sympho, 90, 91
Yair Haklai, 94
KMJ, 99
Jaypee, 107
Ikiwaner, 122
Sujit kumar, 124
David Monniaux, 145
Timjarrett, 192

Public Domain
NASA, 9, 10, 28, 131
Pisano OPA Florence, 19
Zzubnik, 23
First flight, December 17, 1903, 34 (Library of Congress)
CIA, 73
Rodin, 57
Sir Edward Poynter, 58
Buddha Shakyamuni or the Jina Buddha Vairochana, 78-79
Dore, 14, 88
Ricardo630, 97
Detail from the Bayeux Tapestry, 108
GalliasM, 114
Ecclesiastical Figure in Prayer, 116
Strobridge Lith. Co., 118
Wilma Rudolph, 127
GSFC/ NOAA/ USGS, 131
USDA, Scott Bauer, 154, 164, 235
J. & R. Lamb Studios, 160, 190
G. Eric and Edith Matson Photograph Collection, 162
US, 168
Crown Hugo Gerhard Ströhl, 177
Carl Bloch, 178
Francis Grose, 181
Raffaelino del Garbo, 196–197
Renee Comet, 233
USDHH, 233